Henry P. Hill, a graduate of the Wharton School of Finance and Commerce of the University of Pennsylvania, is a partner of Price Waterhouse & Co. He is a C.P.A. of New York and several other states.

Joseph L. Roth, who graduated from Pace College is also a partner of Price Waterhouse & Co. He is a C.P.A. of New York, New Jersey, and several other states.

Herbert Arkin, Ph.D. Columbia University, is Professor of Business Administration and Supervisor of the Business Statistics Division of the Bernard M. Baruch School of Business and Public Administration, the City College of the City University of New York. He is a statistical consultant for several major business firms.

# SAMPLING IN AUDITING

## A Simplified Guide and Statistical Tables

by

HENRY P. HILL, C.P.A.
Partner, Price Waterhouse & Co.

JOSEPH L. ROTH, C.P.A.
Partner, Price Waterhouse & Co.

HERBERT ARKIN, Ph.D.
Baruch School of Business and Civic Administration,
The City College of New York

THE RONALD PRESS COMPANY • NEW YORK

5
NO-B

Library of Congress Catalog Card Number: 62-21811
PRINTED IN THE UNITED STATES OF AMERICA

# PREFACE

This book is designed as a practical guide to the use of statistical sampling in auditing. While this scientific technique has already been found extremely useful in other fields such as industrial quality control, market surveys and in a wide variety of research areas including the sciences, only in the last few years has it been successfully applied in accounting.

As with any other scientific method, the technique cannot be used indiscriminately, nor can it be applied without being specially modified to meet the requirements of the field to which it is being adapted. The same techniques may not be suitable even for the same audit test under different circumstances. When, however, statistical methods used in auditing are appropriate to the objectives, the technique has been found extremely helpful.

Since it cannot be expected that all accountants will become trained statisticians, this book is designed to provide, within its brief text, some aspects of the nature of statistical sampling, and some of the circumstances under which it is most appropriate.

Its main purpose, however, is to provide practical, statistical tables especially designed for auditing, together with step-by-step instructions on how to use these tables without requiring on the part of the auditor a knowledge of the mathematics behind them. For those who might wish to go beyond the application of these precalculated figures, the mathematical formulae from which they were compiled are set forth in the appendix.

Finally, this book concentrates on the sampling methods that appear to the authors to be the most appropriate and useful for the auditor, and it has the advantage of requiring no knowledge of statistical theory, although as in all fields, some knowledge of the basic theory would increase the understanding of the applications and prevent possible misuse of this method. For those who wish to probe more deeply into statistical theory and concepts, more detailed works are suggested in the bibliography.

The basic problems of any practitioner of sampling are:

How to sample,
How much to sample,
How to appraise sample results.

The possible approaches are:

Estimation sampling,
Discovery sampling,
Acceptance sampling.

This book concentrates primarily on the first two approaches, since acceptance sampling is of limited usefulness in the main auditing areas, the term auditing here meaning primarily the examination of financial statements by independent accountants and also the examinations of branches, factories and other outlying locations by internal auditors, and similar examinations. It is not intended to treat here certain auditing processes such as checking quality of clerical output and examining suppliers' invoices for clerical and other accuracy prior to payment.

It is hoped that the accounting practitioner will find the techniques described here useful in the problems ordinarily encountered in his practice. In more complex problems and in areas involving large numbers of transactions where sophisticated techniques, such as stratified or ratio estimate sampling, may give results in savings of considerable magnitude, it may be advantageous to consult a professional statistician.

Henry P. Hill
Joseph L. Roth
Herbert Arkin

October, 1962

# CONTENTS

## CHAPTER 5



## CHAPTER 6



## CHAPTER 7



## TABLES

# SAMPLING IN AUDITING

## A Simplified Guide and Statistical Tables

# Chapter 1

# WHY STATISTICAL SAMPLING?

Every auditor has used the sampling process. However, he has come to know it under a different name—testing or test checking. The method consists of the practice of forming an opinion about a group of items (records, entries, vouchers, etc.) on the basis of an examination of a few of the items.

Statistical sampling consists of the same general process with some refinements. This method is based on the laws of probability and is derived from them through complex mathematical procedures.

The primary purpose of the statistical approach is to provide a more objective result from a sample, together with a means of measuring the reliability of the estimate so obtained.

## TESTING

The Committee on Auditing Procedure of the American Institute of Certified Public Accountants refers to tests of auditors as follows:

". . . . .The auditor's examination of the internal evidential matter is accomplished through his tests. There is no magic formula by which a proper degree of testing may be established any more than there is a uniformly satisfactory method of selecting the audit procedures which are appropriate. Tests made haphazardly are without significance and will be of little comfort to the auditor who is called upon to demonstrate that he has exercised due care in his examination. The objective of testing is to determine whether reliance may be placed upon the examinee's representations as expressed in the books of account and financial statements. The appropriate degree of testing will be that which may reasonably be relied upon to bring to light errors in about the same proportion as would exist in the whole of the record being tested." [1]

As can be seen from this excerpt, the method and degree of testing is left entirely to the auditor. His determination will be based upon his training and experience in the field of auditing.

In 1962, however, the Committee on Statistical Sampling of the American Institute rendered a report [2] which concludes that statistical sampling methods are useful in some audit tests and are permitted under generally accepted auditing procedures. It emphasizes, however, that the choice of testing methods is still left to the judgment of the auditor.

## STATISTICAL SAMPLING

What is statistical sampling? Many auditors mistakenly refer to statistical sampling as random sampling. The two terms should not be confused. The former refers to the whole process of carrying out a test on a scientific basis. The latter is merely a method of selecting the sample to be used. For example, if a test is made to find out whether all checks had been endorsed properly, the sample size must first be determined, the items in the sample then selected and examined and, finally, the likely number of all checks not endorsed properly calculated. The entire process would be referred to as statistical sampling. The selection of the individual checks to be examined, if it were done by using random number tables, would properly be called random sampling. This term includes any acceptable probability selection procedure such as a systematic sampling method.

A statistical sampling plan accordingly embraces three distinct parts, (1) the calculation of sample size, (2) the selection of the

[1] "Generally Accepted Auditing Standards—Their Significance and Scope," Special Report of Committee on Auditing Procedures, American Institute of Certified Public Accountants, New York, 1954, p. 37.

[2] "Statistical Sampling and the Independent Auditor," Special Report by the Committee on Statistical Sampling, American Institute of Certified Public Accountants, published in the *Journal of Accountancy,* February, 1962, p. 60.

sample, and (3) the evaluation of the results. All are accomplished by use of very definite statistical techniques.

When a conclusion is reached from examining only a limited number of items, obviously some risk must be taken. The items selected for the sample might not be perfectly representative, and thus the sample will not produce an accurate image of the true state of affairs. It is also apparent that the fewer items picked, i.e., the smaller the size of the sample, the greater the chance taken and conversely the more items picked, the greater the reliance that can be placed on the sample results. Though recognizing this, the accountant generally has had no way of measuring the effect of the sample size.

## NONSAMPLING ERROR

Before discussing the risks in using a sample established by statistical means, the auditor or sampler must first recognize the possibility or even likelihood that the results obtained may be inaccurate because of mistakes made in inspecting or examining the items in the sample. This is referred to by statisticians as "nonsampling error." Human fallibility being what it is, mistakes will occur either through carelessness or lack of skill in appraising the material. Should the fact that a voucher did not have a receiving report attached be overlooked by the auditor, the conclusion drawn from the sampling will naturally be wrong. Similarly, incorrect counts would result in an incorrect inventory valuation.

Unfortunately, the risk in nonsampling error generally is not subject to measurement. However, this same risk would exist even though the data of the entire field were to be examined one hundred per cent. Actually, there may be less of this kind of error in a sample than in a complete examination since greater pains can be taken to eliminate many of the possibilities of error when the volume to be examined is relatively small. For example, physical inventory counts made on a sample basis by a small team of experienced and interested employees will be much more accurate than counts made by a large number of untrained employees, usually the case when a complete inventory is taken.

## SAMPLING ERROR

By statistical formulas, from some of which the tables in this book have been constructed, it is possible to estimate in advance the sampling error which will result solely from the use of a sample. This estimate is an indication of how close the sample characteristics will be to the actual characteristics of the whole field. The margins of sampling reliability can be fairly close or may be wider depending on the objective of the test.

The degree of *sampling precision,* as it is generally called, is a value added to and subtracted from the sample result. The true answer is expected to lie somewhere between these limits. For example, if a sample is taken to determine the average balance of a number of accounts, it may be found that based upon the sampling plan, the average of all of the accounts is with measurable probability somewhere between $100 and $125. If an average of all of the account balances were actually to be taken, it may happen to be $112. However, it could also be $101 or $124.

To take another example where the test is to determine a characteristic, such as right or wrong, it may be found that 10% of the items in the sample were wrong. Sampling for this purpose is referred to in this book as sampling for relative frequencies, frequency estimates or attribute sampling. If the plan allowed for a precision of plus or minus 2%, it could be concluded only that the true number of total errors was somewhere between 8% and 12%. The precision for this type of sampling is generally stated as a number of percentage points added to and subtracted from the percentage of incident in the sample. It is not a percentage of the incidence. In other words, in the previous example the margin would *not* be 9.8% to 10.2%.

## CONFIDENCE LEVEL

In determining a sample size to achieve a certain degree of precision, it is also necessary to determine the assurance that the actual state of affairs is even within the range stated. This assurance is generally called the *confidence level.* Having already settled for an approximation, auditors are usually puzzled to learn that even this result is not always right, but may be right, say, only 95% of the time or 99% of the time.

To understand this concept requires some knowledge of the basic laws of probability. If a great number of samples were to be chosen from a given field, they would tend to cluster around the true degree of incidence of the field. In most cases, however, some small number of samples would be so extreme that they would be outside the limits of this cluster. By statistical formula it is possible to measure the percentage of times a sample of a given size will evidence a condition which is within the stated range. This eliminates from the result the effect of the few extreme or unusual samples. It can be seen that for a particular sample size the wider the margin of precision, the more assurance that the sample will fall within it, and conversely the more narrow the margin, the smaller the degree of assurance. Obviously either the precision or the confidence level or both can be increased by increasing the sample size.

These are the two considerations involved, i.e. the precision which is the range within which the true answer most likely falls, and the confidence level, which is the likelihood that it will fall within that range. The confidence level is usually expressed as a percentage, being the number of times out of one hundred that the true answer would be contained within the determined margins. The tables in this book provide for confidence levels generally of 95% and 99% and in some cases 99.9%. These are very high levels of assurance and should suit most audit requirements. In fact, less assurance might well be in order in many circumstances, particularly when the auditor is satisfied by his other investigations that the internal controls are good and he needs less assurance.

## DEGREE OF RISK

The question which constantly is raised by accountants who intend to use a statistical sampling technique is the degree of risk, i.e. confidence level, that should be required. Unfortunately, no fixed rule would apply to the many different applications possible in auditing. The acceptable risk depends entirely on the importance of the result to the auditor. An independent auditor making one of his many tests to form an opinion on a client's financial statements would have an entirely different perspective from that of an internal auditor making routine tests, for example, to determine that outgoing bills have been computed properly where errors would mean a loss of revenue to the company. In the latter case it would be natural to expect that a high level of assurance, possibly 95% or 99%, would be required. In the former a lower degree might well be in order.

Since an independent auditor makes many tests, some interrelated with and dependent on other tests, and all varying to some degree because of the effectiveness or ineffectiveness of the internal controls, he is faced with having to use his own judgment in determining the assurance desired. He can only do this by relating the importance of one to another, that is to say, by comparing how much more importance he places on one test to another he is making.

## DEGREE OF PRECISION

With respect to the degree of precision required, again no fixed rule can be established. In fact, a word of warning may be in order. Since certain tables in this book provide for sample size reliabilities ranging from plus or minus 1% to plus or minus 10%, there may be a natural tendency to pick plus or minus 3% or 4% as a happy compromise. However, the range in these or any other tables has no real significance, and the tables could just as well have been prepared to range from 1/10 of 1% to 2%. The precision required should be decided by considering what the resulting range means in terms of its effect on the acceptability of the results to the auditor.

In dollar value estimation this is no great problem. Since the application of the tables provides a dollar value margin, the result can be appraised readily. For example, a total dollar inventory calculated from a statistical sample may amount to $2,500,000 plus or minus $100,000. An auditor would have little trouble in determining whether or not this result is reasonable.

If conservatism is in order, he may insist on using the lower limit.

In sampling for attributes (frequency estimation), it is more difficult to relate the result to its possible effects on the financial statement. However, if the dollar effect of the occurrences is desired, it is then necesary to revert to variables estimate procedures as explained in Chapter 5 on page 43.

## ADVANTAGES OF STATISTICAL SAMPLING

Since each particular audit test which involves test checking or sampling can be the subject of a decision as to whether to rely on "judgment" sampling or to use a statistical sampling method, the advantages of the latter should be considered.

### *Measurement*

The greatest advantage in using a statistical technique is the ability to measure the reliability and degree of assurance which can be placed on the results. Accordingly, after examining the sample, the auditor is in a much better position to form a sound opinion. Where a dollar determination has been made, for example, he knows the range within which the actual amount should fall. Thus, the basis for his conclusions is clearly defensible. However, more importantly than merely defending himself, his ability to evaluate the results of his test furnishes a better basis for his decision. Should he be dissatisfied with the results, he can always enlarge his sample to get more reliable information or more assurance and then reconsider his decision in the light of the new facts.

### *Objectivity*

The second most important advantage of statistical sampling is the objectivity of the approach. Proper selection procedures assure that the test will bring to light a reasonable cross section of the field being examined. Therefore, it provides for disclosing conditions or factors which might not be considered or even known of in choosing a sample by judgment or intuition to say nothing of just plain haphazardly. Particularly in those circumstances where the audit objective is to determine the frequency of the various types of items in the field, the statistical technique is most advantageous.

It might well be pointed out that this objectivity is a result of proper selection techniques and does not involve the determination of sample size or the evaluation of the results. However, if the sample is selected in accordance with proper statistical standards, the auditor is justified in evaluating his results by using the appropriate statistical tables. Generally speaking this involves very little additional time and effort so that it would be foolish to ignore the primary advantage of obtaining a measure of the reliability (precision) and confidence level of the sample. However, the basic objectiveness of the statistical approach is very often the factor which indicates its use in various auditing tests.

### *Effectiveness*

A collateral advantage of applying statistical techniques results from the necessity of establishing in advance the specific objectives of the test and the general nature and characteristics of the field to be examined. In many instances this review of an audit step has brought about a clearer understanding of what was expected to be accomplished by it and in some cases has resulted in reconsidering the audit approach or even the need for the particular step in the first place. Accordingly, the effectiveness of the auditor's examination is frequently improved because of the statistical approach.

Sometimes there is difficulty in pinpointing a specific objective because of the complexity of the audit procedure or its relation to others. Where it appears that several objectives are involved in one test, these several objectives can be considered as separate tests accomplished by using the same sample for each. An example would be the examination of disbursement vouchers where the auditor is checking for approvals, support, authenticity, arithmetical accuracy and accounting treatment, all of which have varying significance to him. In this case the same sample can be used but separate conclusions reached on each of the individual tests.

### *Efficiency*

Since sample sizes required for specified degrees of reliability and accuracy do not increase proportionately to the size of the field to be examined, economies can be effected frequently by using statistical techniques when the field size is very large, for example, 100,000 or more. This opportunity for savings in time should be considered wherever the sample size in the past has been fairly large. Auditors have generally determined the scope of their tests as a per cent of the total. Even when this total was large, there was a feeling that this percentage should be significant. Since this is not the case, much smaller tests can be made. This is particularly true in examining accounts receivable of utilities, department stores, petroleum marketing companies, etc. The requirement, that a fixed percentage of items be checked, is obviously naïve.

## EXTENT OF APPLICATION

A number of public accounting firms have undertaken studies of the application of statistical sampling techniques to their auditing. In many instances, their efforts might still be experimental. In other cases general use may be encouraged depending upon the extent of training of the individual staff members. Similarly, internal auditors of many large companies and government agencies have begun to adopt statistical techniques. Since in most accounting firms the techniques used are left to the individual auditor and the principal or supervisor who reviews his work, there is no basis for determining the extent to which statistical sampling is applied or what particular tests are most suitable for its application. However, many articles have been published on various applications of statistics to auditing circumstances.[3]

[3] See "Glossary of Statistical Terms for Accountants and Bibliography on the Application of Statistical Methods to Accounting and Management Control," A.I.C.P.A., New York, 1958.

In most examinations which an independent auditor conducts to express an opinion on a client's financial statements, there is likely to be at least one test which could be performed more effectively by using statistical sampling techniques regardless of the size of the company. On the other hand, because of the nature of the examination it is unlikely that there would be more than three or four. A substantial part of such an examination is analytical rather than sampling, and a continuing emphasis on the "businessman's approach" [4] to auditing will make these examinations even more so. Statistical methods, however, will be most useful where a decision is required in situations involving a large mass of detail where only relatively small samples can be tested, for example: tests of physical inventory, inventory pricing and extensions; tests of accounts receivable including confirmation, particularly where they consist of numerous relatively small accounts; examination of disbursement vouchers; tests of revenue, particularly in public utilities or other similar organizations where revenue arises from a multitude of small transactions; claim payments in an insurance company; payments from pension and other funds, etc.

[4] "The Business Approach to Auditing," by Zach T. White, *Mass. C.P.A. Review,* January, 1962.

# Chapter 2

# SAMPLING PLANS

Before attempting to explain how to sample and how to use the tables in this book, it may be well to furnish a brief description of the various statistical techniques available to auditors. Since the circumstances of each audit test vary, the auditor should be acquainted with the different methods so that he might develop a suitable plan in each case. It does not follow that a plan developed for a specific test, for example, confirming accounts receivable, will be appropriate for all other tests of that type. Not only may a different selection technique be necessary, but the basic method may be unsuitable. What then, are these methods?

## ACCEPTANCE SAMPLING

Acceptance sampling is a kind of sampling plan long used in industry for distinguishing good lots of purchased materials from bad lots where a bad lot is one which contains more than a specified percentage of defective items. Essentially it consists of a statement that a given number of items will be sampled from a field of a given size and if more than a certain number of defective items are found in the sample, the lot will be rejected.

While early writings in this field have suggested the possibility of using this technique as a sampling plan for audit tests, for a variety of reasons which are explored at length elsewhere,[1] it is believed that the direct application of this method to the audit

[1] See Herbert Arkin, "Statistical Sampling in Auditing," *New York Certified Public Accountant,* Vol. 27, pp. 454–469, July, 1957.

test is highly questionable. For this reason no acceptance sampling tables have been included in this book. However, the various texts on the application of statistical sampling to auditing such as those listed in the bibliography do treat this subject. Since this is a complex subject, a complete discussion is considered beyond the scope of this book.

On the other hand, there are many areas of accounting operations, other than the audit test, in which acceptance sampling is most useful and modified forms of acceptance sampling procedures may be found valuable in audit tests.

Acceptance sampling plans when applied as described above provide a given probability that fields or lots containing a given per cent of errors or defectives will be rejected by the plan. Thus it is possible to select a plan such that fields containing in excess of a certain error rate will have any desired probability of rejection while fields with a low rate of error will have a high probability of acceptance.

Tables published by the Department of Defense[2] provide certain plans which have a high probability of *acceptance* of certain specified rates of error while the well-known Dodge-Romig[3] tables provide plans which have a high probability of rejection of fields containing specified error rates.

The acceptance sampling method provides merely an accept or reject decision and gives no indication of the rate of error occurring in the field. Further, under these plans there is a definite probability that fields containing rates of error less than the specified undesirable level will nevertheless be rejected.

## FREQUENCY ESTIMATION

Frequency estimation is used to determine by sampling the rate of occurrence of certain attributes within prescribed limits of precision and confidence level. This method can be used to determine the portion of the field that does not conform to the

[2] "Sampling Procedures and Tables for Inspection by Attributes," Military Standard 105C Armed Forces Supply Support Center, Department of Defense, 18 July 1961.

[3] H. F. Dodge and N. G. Romig, *Sampling Inspection Tables*, John Wiley & Sons, New York, 1959.

established standards. The sample can also be used to ascertain (within the prescribed limits of reliability) the characteristics of the field, i.e. the various types of items, the frequency of each, etc.

To use this type of plan, the auditor must first determine the degree of precision, i.e. the range of possible occurrences, and the confidence level or degree of assurance required. For example, he must decide beforehand whether he wants a result within plus or minus 1% of the actual rate of occurrence or if he can be satisfied with plus or minus 5%. He must also decide whether he wants assurance that the true state would be within the range of margin selected either nine times out of ten, ninety-five out of one hundred, ninety-nine out of one hundred times, etc.

In choosing the size of the sample to be examined, strangely enough, some idea of the rate of occurrence in the field should be obtained in advance since this is one of the factors which enters into the formula for determining the sample size. How to determine the likely rate of occurrence is explained in a later chapter. The tables included here for estimation sampling plans cover expected rates of occurrence of 10%, 5%, 2% and 50% (Tables 2a to 2h).

These tables provide the sample size needed to achieve the desired result. However, after the sample has been examined, the actual rate of occurrence in the sample is determined. With this information and using Tables 6 or 6a, which show sample reliability for relative frequencies, the actual upper and lower limits of the true rate of occurrence in the field are found. This is the reliability actually achieved rather than that assumed for purposes of establishing the sample size originally. This procedure is explained more fully in Chapter 5.

Since this method of sampling furnishes a description of the field in terms of the rate of occurrence of the characteristic studied within certain limits of reliability and confidence level, it is one of the most useful of the various techniques available. It can be employed in the examination of any type of document where a frequency of deviations or discrepancies is to be determined. For example, it can be used in the examination of disbursement vouchers where the auditor is interested in finding the rate of occurrence of various deviations, such as proper support or approvals of the payments. It can also be used in confirming accounts receivable to determine the frequency of differences between the company's records and those of its customers. Test counts of physical inventory quantities for comparison with detailed book records where available can also be carried out by this method.

In many auditing tests it is not easy to categorize the documents examined as either right or wrong. Each of the various deficiencies noted have more or less significance to the auditor either because of its type or the materiality of the amount involved. In these cases the auditor may be satisfied to know merely that, within certain limits of precision and confidence, the sample examined is illustrative of the whole. He can then reach a decision based upon the picture (or cross section) of the field he gets from his examination of the sample.

## VARIABLES ESTIMATION

The statistical method used to estimate dollar values is known as variables estimation. This is a method of determining, within prescribed limits of precision and confidence level, an aggregate dollar amount of accounting data by determining the average values of a sample. The degree of precision must be determined in advance, i.e. plus or minus so many dollars as well as the confidence level desired, i.e. 90%, 95%, 99%, etc. The auditor should also have some advance knowledge of the field, since the determination of the sample size to achieve a desired result will depend upon the degree of variability of the items comprising the field. For example, if the items range between $50 and $100, the required sample, for the same degree of reliability, would be much smaller than if the items ranged from $1 to $10,000.

The degree of variability which exists in a field is measured by what is called "standard deviation." This is merely a method developed by statisticians to provide a factor in the formulae to allow for the different degrees of variability. The standard deviation factor can be estimated by examining in advance a relatively small sample, about 50 items, obtaining the average range of groups of items and applying a factor from Table 3. This process is explained more fully in Chapter 4.

After the required sample size is determined and the values ascertained, the auditor can then obtain a more precise determination of the sample reliability at the various confidence levels. Tables 3 and 4 are provided for this purpose, and the mechanics are explained in Chapter 5.

This type of sampling plan is very useful in making determinations for accounting purposes. However, there are many opportunities for using it in auditing where the objective of the audit test is to arrive at an approximate dollar figure. It can be used, for example, in determining the aggregate dollar amount of inventories by counting and pricing only a portion of the materials. It can also be used in determining the age of accounts receivable balances. Both of these applications have been used successfully.

The distinction between the use of a frequency estimation plan and a dollar value or variable estimation may be illustrated in the testing of inventories. Where a company maintains perpetual inventory records for each item in inventory, the auditor might make test counts to satisfy himself as to the acceptability of the quantities shown in the records. Since this would involve only determining whether or not each item was in substantial agreement, the test would be for attributes and a frequency estimation plan would be used. However, where a company does not maintain detailed records and the amount of the inventory at a particular date is to be determined from a physical count which would be priced and totaled, a test of the reasonableness of the aggregate inventory could be made by dollar value estimation. In this case, each item in the *sample* would be counted, priced and extended. On the basis of the average value of the items selected, the aggregate value of the inventory could be determined within the limits of reliability attained and compared to the company's determination.

This is the distinction. On the one hand, the auditor's objective was to determine attributes, in this case comparisons with detail records. On the other hand, his objective was to satisfy himself as to an aggregate dollar amount. This illustrates the necessity of understanding the various statistical techniques and applying the proper one in the circumstances.

In the case of inventories the test counts made by auditors to determine the acceptability of the quantity records can often be carried a step further. By determining the dollar value of the items selected and from the average values in the sample, the reasonableness of the aggregate amount of inventory could be ascertained. However, if this is attempted, the sample must be selected in such a way that the groups of items sampled are relatively homogeneous as to value; otherwise, the margin of reliability will be extremely wide. A stratified plan (see Chapter 6) would probably be necessary.

## DISCOVERY SAMPLING

Discovery sampling, which is also called exploratory sampling, is a plan which provides an assurance at a prescribed confidence level of finding at least one deviation, if they exist to a significant extent in the field. This technique is useful where a low percentage of deviations is expected by the auditor because of the effectiveness of the accounting procedures and the internal controls. However, he must satisfy himself that a possible source of error or weakness in the controls has not been overlooked. If he finds one deviation or deficiency, that one would be used as the clue for further investigation to determine the circumstances which permitted it to occur. From this investigation he would learn whether it was an isolated instance or whether the error could be more widespread. If the latter, a more extended sampling plan would probably be needed to obtain, say through estimation sampling, the likely degree of deviation.

Obviously, a reasonable discovery sampling plan would not produce an irregularity if there is only one in a million. In that case a tremendously large sample size would be required. However, there is no effective way of locating the extremely rare occurrence.

There is a corollary conclusion to be drawn from a discovery sampling plan which can be most useful to the auditor. If the plan calls for a certain assurance that one deviation will be discovered, if deviations exist to a certain degree in the field, the incidence of deviation can be considered less than the prescribed degree if no errors are found. For example, if a plan is used which has a 95% assurance of finding an exception if they exist to the extent of .5% of the field and none are discovered, there would be a 95% chance that the degree of errors is less than .5%.

In auditing, for example, discovery sampling plans have been used for such routine tests as checking shipping documents to sales invoices and checking interest on security investments of an investment trust where the volume of such transactions was very large.

Table 5 provides the probabilities of finding at least one occurrence in various field sizes and the required sample size. These are given for various percentages of occurrences in the field. Should the examination of the sample not produce any occurrences, Tables 6b and 6c indicate the maximum rate of occurrences which could exist depending upon the sample size and the field size for confidence levels 95% and 99%. The procedures are described more fully in Chapter 5.

It should be remembered that in each of the estimation sampling techniques described above, the job is not done when the sample size is selected. The accuracy and confidence levels actually attained must be re-evaluated after the sample has been examined. This means two things: first the frequency or dollar averages of items in the samples must be determined and, second, from this result the margins of reliability must be computed at the confidence level desired. An illustration of how to carry out a sampling plan in an actual audit is included as Chapter 7.

# Chapter 3

## HOW TO SAMPLE

The "how" of the sampling method is of prime importance. The mechanics of sampling may well decide the success or failure of the test in providing the auditor with the desired assurance. Mathematical theory can provide protection in the interpretation of the results of samples only if the sample is drawn on a "probability" basis.

All tables discussed in this manual are based on the assumption that the samples used are what the statistician would term "probability" samples. These are sometimes called "random" samples. *Haphazard choices or judgment selection of a sample completely invalidates the use of the tables with respect to that sample.* The samples must be obtained as "random samples," which require the use of random number tables or systematic sampling.

Randomness provides not only an objective and defensible choice of the sample items (since it entirely removes from the auditor the choice of the items to be checked), but also a complete surprise element which cannot be circumvented by the fraud-minded individual, as well as an assurance of the desired representativeness achieved by mathematical theory.

It might be well to define the term "random choice." Essentially, it means that each of the items in the group or sub-group being sampled has an equal opportunity for inclusion in the sample. Haphazard choice without conscious intent to be selective does not provide randomness, nor does it provide the basis for the application of the mathematical theory of probability upon which these tables rest. The selection of items to be included in the sample can easily be biased without deliberate intent.

How then can a truly random and unbiased choice be made? Several methods are available. Two major classifications of these methods may be made:

Random number sampling
Systematic sampling

Further, these two methods of drawing the individual items to be included in the sample may be applied in several different ways, including:

A. *Unrestricted random sampling* which consists of selecting individual units at random from those comprising the entire field.
B. *Stratified random sampling* which consists of dividing the field into separate parts or strata and randomly sampling from each strata on an independent basis.
C. *Cluster sampling* which consists of selecting *groups* of items randomly.

## RANDOM NUMBER SAMPLING

In its simplest form, unrestricted random sampling would consist of thoroughly mixing up the slips representing the entries to be sampled in a hat, and grabbing a handful—not a very practical approach, and one which can be biased if great care is not exercised. Better methods of accomplishing this end have been provided by tables of random numbers. If the documents of entries to be sampled have been numbered, such as account number, page number, etc., or can be counted, this method may be used.

A Table of Random Digits may be seen following page 57. The sampler may combine the digits shown to provide a number of sufficient digits to cover the range of the item numbers to be sampled. For instance, if the records to be sampled range in number from 2622 to 8865, a four-digit number will be used. The necessary four-digit numbers are obtained by combining columns of random digits in any manner. While the digits in this table are grouped in fives for the purpose of ease in reading, any groups of four may be used. Thus, starting with the first column of groupings of random numbers, the first sample number may be taken as the last four digits of the group, or 0480 (first column, first row of random numbers). This record or entry will then be included in the sample. The next item number to be selected is 2368 (first column, second row), etc.

If a sample number outside the range of the numbers to be used is encountered, it is ignored, and the next number is used in its place. If a duplicate number arises, it is ignored. The numbers drawn then comprise the numbers of the items in the sample.

A start in the random number table may be at any random point. However, care must be exercised to avoid the use of the same starting point for later tests of the same materials.

The most practical approach to the mechanics of such sampling is to copy each random number to be used on a card or slip of paper, and to sort these numbers into numerical sequence for the actual pulling of the items to be sampled. However, the sample items can be secured without this step, although it may be less convenient.

If more random numbers are needed, due to duplicate random numbers which have been discarded or because the series of document numbers are not continuous and some of the selected random numbers cannot be used, then additional random numbers (next in sequence in the random number table) may be drawn to make up the deficiency. If it is desired to enlarge the original sample, additional random numbers may be drawn and the items so designated added to the previously obtained sample. Several tables of random numbers are listed in the bibliography on page 57.

## SYSTEMATIC SAMPLING

Where items are not or cannot be numbered or the costs of pulling the selected documents individually are too great, systematic sampling may be used. Systematic sampling consists of selecting every *nth* item out of the series of entries or records, using a random start. For instance, if accounts receivable are being sampled for the purpose of confirmation, and a sample of 200 accounts out of 4,000 is desired, every 20th account may be used by selection from a list or file of these accounts *provided the starting point is a random selection and the entire file is covered.*

This method may be more simple to apply than the use of random numbers, but there are certain inherent dangers when the method is not carefully used. Great care must be exercised that there is no arrangement of the sequence of entries that might introduce a bias into the sample. For instance, a list of accounts numbered in a series that allows space for new accounts by leaving certain numbers unused at regular intervals raises the possibility that a systematic sample if taken with a certain start and at a certain interval may consist of all new accounts or no new accounts.

While this example provides indication of one apparent danger, there are other instances when less obvious dangers of bias are introduced by the arrangement of the items. In certain types of numbering systems, the sampling interval must be selected carefully to prevent bias by the inclusion of an undue proportion of certain types of accounts or items. For example, if large customers are given numbers ending in zeros, a plan that would fall naturally on these would be biased. It would also be biased if it resulted in picking none of the large items.

However, there are techniques which can overcome these difficulties. For instance, avoidance of the effect of a cyclical or periodic arrangement can be accomplished by using several random starts with the use of every *nth* item after each start. In such cases, the sampling interval for each start will be larger to provide the same sample size. If the sequence of items shows no cyclical arrangement, or if there is at least some assurance to that effect, systematic sampling will be as good an approach as that attained through random numbers.

Because of these dangers, unrestricted random sampling (use of random numbers) must be considered preferable.

Those not experienced in the use of random number tables tend to use systematic sampling since it seems simpler. In actual practice random selection is usually quicker as well as preferable. For example, if a sample of two hundred is to be selected from a field of sixty thousand, in systematic sampling every three hundredth item would be selected. To count to three hundred, two hundred different times requires quite an effort. If it is at all possible, a numbering system should be devised so that random numbers can be used.

A few possibilities will illustrate how to devise a numbering system for use with random numbers. For instance, if the items are contained on a listing, tabulating machine or otherwise, numbers can be assigned to each page and to each line on a standard page. The numbers do not actually have to be written alongside each item but a method can be adopted by which items can be identified merely by count. Random numbers can then be selected within the range of the number of pages and number of lines, i.e. if there are less than 100 pages and less than 100 items on a page, four digit numbers would be selected. The first two would indicate the page, and the second two the item on the page to be selected. Numbers which do not fit the scheme would be ignored.

Should the documents be numbered but a new series of numbers started each month, random numbers should be picked which have two digits more than the number of digits in the numbering system. These two digits would be limited to 01 to 12 and would indicate the month of the voucher. Similarly, should letters be involved, two digits representing the twenty-six letters of the alphabet could be chosen.

## STRATIFIED SAMPLING

Another important consideration when the auditor attempts a test is the fact that he may not consider all accounts or records of equal importance. For instance, he may have a much greater interest in establishing the accuracy of large accounts and thus be unwilling to run as great a sampling risk for this type of account. Objective sampling methods do not of necessity require sampling from a general pool of all items. It is not only possible but often desirable to segregate accounts into separate groups, say by size or other characteristics, and to sample to various degrees of accuracy in each area separately.

For example, it may be desirable to audit all accounts with balances of more than a certain amount and to sample others—a common and perfectly valid practice, providing all sampling is objective. This technique of using separate sampling ratios for different groups of items is known as stratified sampling. A more detailed discussion is included in Chapter 6.

When the bulk of values to be sampled falls within a given range, but a small number of unusually high values are included (technically, a skewed distribution), stratified sampling may be a virtual necessity if the sample is designed to establish an average or total value. In such a case the few large values are included in their entirety, while the balance of the values are sampled.

Stratification can be used not only to segregate items to be examined completely, as for instance, the large items mentioned, but also to segregate types of items which are not to be examined at all—in other words, to ignore items too insignificant or of no interest for purposes of the audit step.

If the field to be examined is composed of types of items of widely varying significance, it may be difficult to apply a statistical sampling technique which will accomplish the original objective of the test. For example, a field of disbursement vouchers may contain many small items of no particular significance; a relatively few vouchers for major disbursements for materials; and still fewer for major advertising expenditures, legal fees and other professional services. These latter usually are important to the auditors. To attempt to stratify the field so as to get a reasonable representation of all the various types in which the auditor may be interested undoubtedly would be inefficient. The apparent solution to this problem would be to select by other means a number of the various types of special significance not represented with great frequency. As a separate test, a sample would be selected by statistical means from the remaining vouchers to cover all other types of disbursements of somewhat equal significance.

This same problem may arise in almost any audit test. For the most effective use of statistical sampling techniques, the field must be constituted of more or less homogenous items about which a conclusion can be reached from a truly objective sample. If the items vary widely, a larger sample size would be required to get a fair representation of all types. This may be better understood by remembering that in dollar value estimation, the results are much more accurate when the range of the items in a particular field or strata is small.

Some care must be exercised in establishing the strata. They should be determined so as to group items which have similar characteristics, bearing in mind the objective of the particular audit test. Dollar amount may not always be the determining factor. Let us look at an actual example. In sampling a physical inventory, strata were established on the basis of unit cost, those with the higher amounts being sampled more extensively and the others less. This seemed quite logical. However, in testing the results, it was found that the largest differences (in total dollar amount) were not in the high unit cost items but in those with the greatest turnover. Since there were many more transactions, there was more exposure to errors in issues, recording, etc. Accordingly, in subsequent tests the degree of turnover was also used in establishing the strata.

## CLUSTER SAMPLING

The auditor sometimes employs other methods of sampling which can be developed to serve as a probability or random sample.

One of these methods is the "cluster" sample. This method consists of selecting groups of contiguous items or records for test purposes. Since this is an easier method of securing sample items, it is often used.

If the clusters are selected by random methods such as those previously outlined, the result may be considered a probability or random sample.

For this purpose, sampling may be accomplished, as before, through the use of random numbers or systematic sampling, except that the sample item selected in each instance will be considered the first item of a group of the desired size, and a sufficient number of following items used to make up the required group size.

*However, if this method of sampling is employed, the tables in this manual for sample size and sample appraisal should not be used unless special methods, such as those outlined in Chapter 6, are applied.*

Cluster samples, or the sampling of groups of items, generally result in less efficient samples than items sampled individually and will usually require larger sample sizes to achieve the same goal. Thus, the savings in using this type of sample may be an illusion. The auditor should, therefore, consider alternate plans before adopting this technique.

Auditors frequently select a particular period, a single payroll, a specified location or a single ledger as the basis for a test. A sample of all or part of such a group of entries is *not* to be confused with a cluster sample. Even if such a period or group is selected by random methods, this does not provide an adequate sample of anything except that particular period, payroll, ledger, etc. This approach is discussed more fully later.

## GENERAL CONSIDERATIONS

The success of sampling will depend upon the proper definition of the field to be sampled. Careful consideration of the objectives of the test will enable the auditor to decide on his definition of the field.

For instance, if certain entries originating at several different field offices of the same business organization are to be tested, decision must be reached whether the objective is to test the over-all set of records or to formulate judgments about differences among the several originating offices.

In the first case, the entire group of entries from all offices is one field to be sampled randomly; in the other, the entries for each office constitute a separate field—each to be sampled individually.

In specifying his objective, the auditor must determine exactly what constitutes an item sampling unit. It is an advantage to have the field constituted of the smallest element possible because once a field reaches several thousand, the sample size increases very slowly. Thus, if consistent with the objective, the auditor may be able to design his plan to take advantage of this fact. For example, in examining vouchers, it may be possible to select only so many invoices or even line items on an invoice rather than approximately the same amount of complete vouchers.

The auditor must also determine in advance what is to be considered an exception or deviation. This, of course, will depend on the individual test and its objective. For example, in a test designed to determine the reasonableness of an amount which appears directly on the financial statements, only those factors which, if they occur with great frequency, would have a significant effect on the balance would be considered an exception. On the other hand, in a test designed to determine the effectiveness of the accounting procedures, any deviation from those prescribed would likely be so considered.

This determination must be made before selecting the sample as it will have a bearing on the expected rate of occurrence. In accounting, the incidents of error are generally few and the field is divided into a great number of regular items and only a small proportion of irregular items. For this reason tables have been provided herein for relatively low rates of occurrences. These are more appropriate for auditors than those prepared for general use which assume the worst situation, that is a 50–50 division and require larger sample sizes.

Any selection plan must be considered carefully before being used since the wrong approach can waste considerable time and effort. Sometimes some ingenuity may be required but in most cases ordinary common sense suffices. For example, to try to sample physical inventories by selecting items from listings or by tag number might require hours in locating the individual items in the plant. Instead, it may be possible to divide the entire count area into small units and to select samples of these units.

## TESTING A SELECTED PERIOD OR AREA

It is common practice in auditing to use as the basis for a test a sample selected from the entries for a particular month, week, or day (or all of the data for that limited period). Upon occasion, the selection of a period such as the year and date is deliberate to validate a balance as of that time. However, the period of time may have been chosen because it was considered a sample of the entire year.

The result of such a sampling, provided an objective sample has been used, is a perfectly valid evaluation of the accuracy of these records for the period sampled, but it may be applied to that month, week or day *only,* and does not of necessity apply to the rest of the year. Statistical methods may *not* be used to extend the results of the sample to the portion of the year not tested. Other auditing techniques must be used for that purpose and the auditor will get no protection from the statistical methods.

In a similar manner, when auditing an organization with a broad geographical distribution, it is not uncommon to select records or entries of a limited area as a basis for their sampling. Again, statistically derived conclusions based on such a sample are applicable to that area alone.

As a further example, consider the case of the company with a large number of bank accounts and the problem of their reconciliation. Shall a sample of the accounts be taken by randomly selecting a month and reconciling a sample of accounts for that month? The question here relates to the definition of the field. Actually, assurance as to the accuracy of all statements for all months may be the objective. Thus, if there are 100 accounts, the field actually investigated is one of 1,200, i.e. 100 accounts for each of 12 months and the sampling must be accomplished by random selection from the 1,200 sampling units, not the 100 accounts for one month. The auditor making his selection from one month will have to justify his conclusions that the accounts have been properly reconciled during the entire year *by other than statistical methods.*

# Chapter 4

# HOW MUCH TO SAMPLE

## THE APPROPRIATE SAMPLE SIZE

The determination of appropriate sample sizes is a function of the objectives of the sampling as well as of the risk to be undertaken.

The purposes of a test or sample in auditing vary but generally will be the determination of one of the following:

Extent of failures to conform to prescribed internal control procedures and/or established accounting practices.
Frequency of occurrence of material errors.
Evidence of fraud or manipulations.
An estimate of the dollar value of a certain class of items, such as overdue accounts receivable.

The sampling method may be different in each case. For instance, in examining extent of failures to conform to internal control, the objective may be to ascertain the relative frequency of departures from prescribed procedures or merely to sample sufficiently to find at least one example of such a departure if it does occur. The same may be true of the other areas. However, in the case of fraud or manipulations, it may be sufficient to find just *one* instance in order to precipitate an investigation.

As outlined above, the two possible approaches of greatest value to the independent auditor are:

*Estimation sampling* which has as its objective the determination, within specified reliability or precision limits, of the frequency of occurrence or the magnitude of certain events or values such as errors.

*Discovery sampling* which has as its objective the provision of adequate assurance of locating an example of some kind of event such as a material error or manipulation, if it occurs with some minimum frequency.

## ESTIMATION SAMPLING

As noted previously, the function of estimation sampling is to determine within specified limits and with a specified risk the frequency of occurrence of some event such as errors, violations of internal controls, etc. or the magnitude of certain values such as errors.

*a. Frequency Estimations (Attributes)*

The objective here is the determination from a sample of how often a particular occurrence has taken place. Thus the estimation methods described in this section apply to estimation of the frequency of occurrence of some event that can be expressed as a per cent of the total. An example might be the percentage of disbursement vouchers not supported by proper receiving reports. The sample size required to estimate such a characteristic within some limits (say ± 2% of the true but unknown percentage) with a given degree of confidence (risk) may be determined by reference to Table 2.

To use Table 2, as all other tables, a random sample must be contemplated. A decision will have to be reached as to how close it is necessary to estimate the "true" percentage of error or other specified events.

Thus, an auditor wishing to determine the frequency of failures to support disbursement vouchers with proper receiving documents would decide on how close it is necessary to establish this percentage. He may be satisfied with an estimate to within ± 2% of the actual frequency of occurrence. Of course, he can make this allowable sampling variation as small as he may desire, but the smaller the allowable sampling variability, the greater the sample necessary.

He will then decide on the confidence level or risk he is willing to run in sampling. This he may fix at 95% or 99% if he used the accompanying tables. A confidence level of 99% means that there are 99 chances out of 100 that the percentage found in the sample will actually be within the desired limits (say ± 2% from the "true" frequency as above). Once the desired precision and risk are established, the sample size required to secure these characteristics may be determined from the table.

However, the sample size required is a function of the actual per cent (say, of error) in the data sampled. Of course, this is unknown. Nevertheless, it is possible to secure a tentative approximation of the sample size required by using a figure for frequency of occurrence, which is larger than that in the records, or a percentage considered excessive up to a maximum of 50%. The usual sampling tables prepared for the use of statisticians are based upon the assumption of a 50% occurrence, which results in the maximum sample size. This is excessive for auditors, since percentages of this magnitude of errors are far beyond any tolerable level.

For purposes of sample size determination, the auditor may use a rate of occurrence which he is reasonably sure will not be exceeded but which is the lowest rate which will meet this requirement.

Use of a conservative approximation will result in an *overstatement of the necessary sample size,* if the actual percentage of occurrence later develops to be less than the figure used, or *underestimation if the actual occurrence* rate is unusually high.

This method will yield an approximate determination of the size of sample needed to achieve the desired precision. However, the appraisal of the sample by methods outlined later will determine the actual reliability achieved by the sample. If the error rate is higher than the high percentage initially selected for the purpose, the need for further action will be evident to the auditor.

To estimate the sample size required to achieve a given sample reliability at a given confidence level in estimating a per cent (Table 2), the following steps are required:

1. Select a level of per cent frequency beyond that likely to occur.
2. Decide on sampling reliability (precision) desired (± 1%, ± 2%, etc.)

3. Select a confidence level (risk) which the auditor is willing to undertake (either 95% or 99% if these tables are used).
4. Determine the field size (number of documents, entries, or other sampling units from which sampling is to be performed).

Given the above, the estimated sample size can be determined as follows:

a. In Table 2 find the page for occurrence rate determined in 1. above (pages for 2%, 5%, 10% and 50% are provided in this book). The 50% table is to be used only when the auditor is unwilling or unable to fix a maximum occurrence rate. It fixes the maximum required sample size regardless of the actual occurrence rate.

b. Select appropriate page for confidence level (95% or 99%).

c. Find line for field size.

d. Find column for sample reliability (± 1%, ± 2%, etc.).

e. At intersection of column and row, sample size is given.

For instance, if a reliability of ± 2% is desired, with a confidence level of 95% for a field of 10,000 items where it is expected that the occurrence rate will not exceed 10%, the sample size is 795 (Table 2a). If, for the same conditions, it was expected that the occurrence rate would not exceed 5%, the sample size would be 436 (Table 2c). The importance of not setting the maximum rate of occurrence likely to be encountered unnecessarily high may be seen in the effect on the sample sizes required in the example.

*b. Dollar Value Estimations (Variables)*

The objective of this method is to estimate an *average* value of a group of items by means of a sample with an assurance equivalent to the confidence level that the sample average will be within a range of some specified amount from the true average which would have been attained if all items in the entire field had been averaged. If a total is to be estimated, the sample average reliability limits may be multiplied by the number of items in the field.

Such estimates may be of value in estimating the dollar value of errors, the total dollar amount of a certain type of account (such as receivables), the dollar value of the difference between physical and book inventories, the dollar value of an inventory, etc. Actually, these estimates need not be confined to dollar value estimates, but may be applied to an average of any value, as, for instance, the average age of accounts receivable.

Once again, the sample must be obtained by random sampling methods such as those previously described. *The techniques described here do not apply to samples obtained by haphazard or judgment sampling methods.* The sample must be selected as explained in Chapter 3.

The size of a sample necessary to achieve a given reliability (± $10, ± $100, ± $1,000, etc.) with a specified risk may be obtained through the use of Table 4.

Just as it is necessary in attributes sampling to estimate in advance the frequency of occurrence, so in variables sampling it is necessary to have some kind of estimate of the variability (standard deviation) of the values in the field to be sampled. One of the methods to obtain this variability estimate is to make a *random* sample of about 50 items from the field to be sampled. These preliminary sample values are then separated into groups of 6 or 7 values. These items must be grouped in the order of occurrence of their original random sequence. If the random numbers used have been arranged in sequence to facilitate locating the sample items, they must be returned to their original random sequence before grouping.

The range (difference between highest and lowest value) is obtained for each group of 6 or 7 items and these ranges are averaged for all groups. The resulting average range may then be *divided* by the $d_2$ factor in Table 3 to obtain the measure of variability (standard deviation). This value is then used in conjunction with Table 4 in order to estimate the required sample size.

Table 4 indicates, for a given field size and confidence level, the sample size estimated to be needed to achieve a given precision. To make the tables more flexible, the precision is expressed as a proportion of the estimated standard deviation.

To estimate the sample size required for a given sample reliability at a given confidence level in estimating an average value (or total value if multiplied by the number of items in the field), Tables 3 and 4 may be used. The following steps are required:

1. Decide on the sampling reliability or precision required per item, on the average (± \$1.00, ± \$10.00, ± \$100.00, etc.).
2. Select a confidence level (risk) which the auditor is willing to take (95%, 99%, or 99.9% if these tables are used).
3. Determine the field size (number of values or entries from which the sample is to be drawn).

Given the above, the estimated sample size can be determined as follows:

a. Obtain a preliminary *random* sample of about 50 items. The preliminary sample may be the first part of the ultimate sample to be used. Additional items may be sampled and added to the preliminary sample to secure the final sample, if later found necessary by these computations.

b. Group these items into groups of 6 or 7 items each, according to the order in which they occurred in the table of random numbers and secure the range of the values for each group (difference between largest and smallest).

c. Secure the averages of these ranges.

d. Using Table 3, obtain the appropriate $d_2$ factor. Divide the average range by this $d_2$ factor to obtain an estimate of the standard deviation.

e. Using Table 4 for the given field size and confidence level, the sample size can be estimated by determining the proportion of the standard deviation which will give the desired reliability. On the line with that proportion, the appropriate sample size is given.

For instance, let it be assumed that it is desired to check the total value of a group of inventory items numbering 5,000 to determine the reasonableness of the book value of these items which is stated as \$4,256,821.68, by using a sample and estimating that total value.

An estimate with an accuracy of about ± 5% of the true total value or about ± \$200,000 is assumed to be sufficiently accurate for the purpose and a 95% confidence level is to be used. This means that the average value per item must be established to within ± \$40.00 (\$200,000 divided by 5,000).

A preliminary random sample of the balances of 48 accounts is secured. Assume the following results when arranged in random groups of 6 each:

| | | | |
|---|---|---|---|
| $1,233.42 | $ 193.96 | $ 790.91 | $ 441.82 |
| 385.20 | 315.99 | 1,677.53 | 1,096.58 |
| 884.53 | 1,301.43 | 1,118.19 | 506.04 |
| 1,467.48 | 858.52 | 846.12 | 492.03 |
| 646.47 | 1,149.00 | 1,191.81 | 627.27 |
| 522.84 | 1,062.17 | 1,088.18 | 995.76 |
| $ 264.00 | $ 955.75 | $1,108.58 | $ 356.00 |
| 331.99 | 1,019.76 | 264.77 | 1,887.99 |
| 1,257.82 | 0 | 404.01 | 1,096.98 |
| 1,220.61 | 1,024.96 | 1,120.59 | 418.01 |
| 1,290.63 | 1,052.17 | 734.49 | 685.25 |
| 926.54 | 1,046.17 | 1,306.64 | 953.75 |

The ranges (differences between highest and smallest value) for these groups of 6 values are:

| | | | |
|---|---|---|---|
| $1,082.28 | $1,107.47 | $ 886.62 | $ 654.76 |
| $1,026.63 | $1,052.17 | $1,041.87 | $1,531.99 |

The average of these eight ranges is $1,047.97. Reference is now made to Table 3 where the factor for group size 6 is found to be 2.534. The average range ($1,047.97) is divided by this factor (2.534) to yield an estimate of the population standard deviation of $413.56.

The precision required here is ± $40.00. Dividing this desired precision (± $40.00) by the above estimate of the standard deviation, $413.56, the result obtained is .097.

Reference may now be had to Table 4, which is entered for field size 5,000. In the column "ratio of sampling error to standard deviation," the value .097 (in this case, use .10, the nearest value) is located. In the column headed 95% confidence level on that row, the required sample size is found to be 357.

It may then be estimated that, for this inventory, a random sample of 357 out of the 5,000 items will give an estimate of the true average value of the 357 items sampled to within $40.00 per item, and for the total value of all accounts, to within ± $200,000.00 (or $40.00 × 5,000) with 95% confidence level.

The preliminary sample of 48 is included as part of the sample taken, thus requiring 309 additional sample values.

The average value of the items in the sample is multiplied by the *total* number of accounts in the field (5,000) to secure the total value.

## DISCOVERY SAMPLING

Upon occasion the auditor may have a different objective in mind. Instead of desiring to determine the sample size required to attain a given degree of accuracy in estimating either the frequency of occurrence or of some total or average value, he may desire to sample sufficiently to assure himself that if some kind of critical event, such as a certain type of failure to conform to internal control or a manipulative event, took place, he will have a reasonable assurance of finding at least one example of such an event in his sample.

It is apparent that if such an event happens only once in a million entries, he is not going to have reasonable assurance of finding an example of it in any reasonable size sample. To find the "needle in the haystack" kind of event, nothing short of 100% inspection will do.

On the other hand, if the auditor is willing to be satisfied in finding an event if it occurs with at least some specified frequency, say 1 in 100 or 1 in 1,000 times, a sample size necessary to give him any desired degree of assurance of locating at least one example of it may be established, if random sampling is used. The sample sizes required for this purpose are shown in Table 5.

To fix the sample size required to find at least one example of a certain type of event in the sample, the following steps are necessary:

1. Decide on the frequency of occurrence of this event which would cause concern and require finding an example.
2. Decide on the degree of assurance (risk) required.
3. Determine the field size.

Given the above, the required sample size can be determined as follows:

a. In Table 5 find the appropriate field size.
b. Use the column When Occurrence Rate is: corresponding to the frequency determined in 1. above.

c. Select a degree of assurance figure (percentage) satisfactory as determined in 2. above.
d. Find the sample size in that row.

For instance, if it is desired to find an example of a failure to secure an authorizing signature on some type of document from among 3,000 of these documents if such failures occur in 0.5% or more of the documents or more frequently with 9 chances out of 10 (90%) of including *at least* one of these failures in the sample, Table 5 may be entered for field size 3,000. Under the column headed 0.5% the figure 90% is sought. It may be seen by reference to the row for sample size that a sample size slightly in excess of 400 would be necessary.

The interpretation of the results of such sampling when no instances of the type sought are found is discussed in Chapter 5 (page 39).

# Chapter 5

## HOW TO APPRAISE SAMPLE RESULTS

The sample sizes obtained by reference to the previous tables are *approximations* of the sample size required to achieve a given degree of reliability of estimation. The reason exact sample sizes cannot be given in advance is that the accurate sample size needed is dependent upon the actual characteristics of the values sampled.

For instance, to determine the precise sample size required for an estimate of the relative frequency of some event in a field in advance, it is necessary to know something about the actual frequency of occurrence in the field, the very fact which we wish to determine by sampling.

To overcome this difficulty, the method suggested, in absence of such knowledge, is to estimate this frequency as some excessive value (see page 30).

In like fashion, for estimating dollar and other values, some knowledge of the field is necessary to estimate the required sample sizes and is obtained by means of a preliminary sample.

However, both of these methods yield approximations which may result in a sampling reliability actually less or greater than that predicted. Upon occasion, when the unexpected develops, the reliability obtained may depart appreciably from that predicted. To provide protection against such poor approximations, it is necessary to appraise the reliability of the sample results *after the sample is drawn.*

Such appraisals of the reliability of results obtained from samples may be accomplished *whether or not* a preliminary approximation of sample size was used. This includes samples based on arbitrarily determined sample sizes. However, these methods may be used *only if random sampling methods previously described have been used in selecting the items to be included in the sample.*

## APPRAISAL OF FREQUENCY ESTIMATES (ATTRIBUTES)

Given a random ("probability") sample of a given size drawn from a given field size, it is possible to appraise the sampling reliability of the relative frequency of an event computed from that sample with any desired degree of assurance (confidence level).

In other words, for such a percentage computed from a sample, it is possible to establish how far from the "true" percentage for all of the values this sample estimate is because of sampling variations, with any degree of assurance desired. Table 6 provides the necessary basis for such an appraisal.

To appraise the reliability of such a percentage computed *from a random sample* of a given size, the following steps are required:

1. From the sample at hand compute the percentage frequency of occurrence of the type of event of interest (errors, etc.).
2. Specify the sample size used and the field size from which it was obtained.
3. Select an appropriate degree of assurance (confidence level). Table 6 provides two such confidence levels. Table 6 indicates values for a 95% confidence level and Table 6a for a 99% confidence level. The confidence level will indicate the probability that the true percentage actually will be included in the range of sampling reliability given.
4. In Table 6 (for 95% confidence level) or Table 6a (for 99% confidence level) find the section headed with the percentage closest to that established by the sample (i.e. table heading Rate of Occurrence in Sample 3%). If sample percentage falls between two sections of the table, always use the next highest value (i.e. for sample percentage of 2.4% use section headed 3%).
5. Using the row appropriate to the field size and the appropriate column for the sample size, the sampling reliability of the sample percentage may be found at the intersection.

a. The table indicates the limits within which the true rate of occurrence of the field may be expected to be found with the probability (confidence level) indicated.

As an illustration of the use of this method, assume that a random sample of 300 observations has been taken from a field of 10,000 entries and that the frequency of occurrence of some type of error is established as 2% for the sample. The sampling reliability of this 2% estimate for a 95% confidence level may be established as follows:

1. The percentage frequency of this type of error is estimated from the sample to be 2%.
2. The sample size used is known to be 300 from a field of 10,000 entries.
3. A confidence level or degree of assurance of 95% was selected. Therefore, Table 6 is used.
4. In Table 6 the section headed Rate of Occurrence in Sample 2% is used, since this is the same as the sample estimate.
5. The row in this section of Table 6 for field size 10,000 is located and the column for sample size 300 is found. At the intersection of this column and row, the true field value may be expected to be within the limits 0.9% and 4.2%.

It may be concluded that there are 95 chances out of 100 that the frequency of error which would have been determined by examining all the entries rather than a sample would be between 0.9% and 4.2%. The auditor will have to decide whether this is a satisfactory condition.

In the special case in which a sample discloses no events of the type being checked (0.0% of occurrences), Table 6b (for a 95% confidence level) and Table 6c (for 99% confidence level) will be used. These tables provide the maximum field per cent of occurrences that might still give rise to such a sample with no occurrences.

For instance, Table 6b gives for field size 1,000 and sample size 100, a value of 2.8%. This may be interpreted as meaning that for such a field or sample size there is a 95% probability that the actual field per cent is that stated (2.8%) or below or, in other words, there are less than 5 chances in 100 that the field could have contained in excess of 2.8% of such occurrences and yet have given rise to a sample containing no occurrences.

## APPRAISAL OF DOLLAR VALUE ESTIMATES (VARIABLES)

Given an average value (dollar or other quantity) computed from a random sample of a given size drawn from a field consisting of a given number of entries, it is possible to appraise the sample reliability of the average with any desired degree of assurance (confidence level). The sampling reliability of the *total* value of a field can, in turn, be established by multiplying both the estimated average and its reliability range by the number of items *in the field.*

Since the sampling reliability of an average is dependent not only upon the sample size and the field size, but, as previously noted, also upon the amount of variability of the values in the field, it is necessary to obtain a firmer estimate of this variability than that used when estimating sample sizes.

The estimated sample size may provide more or less sampling reliability than that anticipated, depending on how close the actual variability in the field is to that estimated on the basis of a preliminary sample (see page 32). If the sample size was selected arbitrarily without the use of a technique such as that previously described, the method discussed below will be a way of obtaining appraisal of sample reliability.

It will be recalled (page 32) that the method used to measure the variability of the field (as indicated by the standard deviation) was to obtain preliminary random sample groups of 6 or 7 items and to secure the average range of these groups. This average range was then divided by an appropriate factor (see Table 3) to obtain the desired estimate of variability (as expressed by its standard deviation).

Upon completion of the drawing of the entire sample, there will now be available a large series of randomly selected values which may now be used for obtaining a more precise estimate of this variability. Grouping all (or if this is impracticable because of a very large sample size, at least 100) of the items in the sample into groups of 6 or 7, the average range may be obtained as before, an appropriate factor selected from Table 3, and the standard deviation estimated by dividing the average range by this factor. Table 7 will now provide a basis for determining the sample reliability of the average obtained from the sample. This table provides three confidence levels: 95%, 99% and 99.9%.

To appraise the reliability of an average value computed from a random sample, the following steps are required:

1. From the sample at hand, compute the average value.
2. Specify the sample size used and the field size from which it was obtained.
3. Select a confidence level (degree of assurance) which will satisfy the auditor (95%, 99% or 99.9%, if these tables are used).
4. Group the values which comprise the sample (or at least 100 of them) into groups of 6 or 7, using the original order of their occurrence in the random number table or their systematic selection. The arrangement will be facilitated if the slips on which the random numbers are entered to be subsequently sorted into file sequence also contain the original sequence number of each random number used. Entry of the values for each entry on the slip with its random number and sorting back into original sequence according to this number will provide the required grouping.
5. Obtain the range of each group of 6 or 7. The range is the difference between the largest and smallest value in each group.
6. Obtain the average range for all groups.
7. Divide this average range by the factor obtained from Table 3. The factor will be dependent upon the number of items included in each group. The result will be an estimate of the standard deviation.
8. In Table 7 find the section for the appropriate field size and the line for the sample size.
9. Select the column for the previously selected confidence level (95%, 99% or 99.9%). On that line in this column the sampling reliability is expressed as a decimal of the estimated standard deviation. By multiplying the estimate of the standard deviation as obtained in 7 above by this decimal value, the sampling reliability (in terms of dollars or other units used) will result.

This resulting value should be measured plus and minus about the average estimated from the sample to obtain an interval or range within which there is a probability equal to the confidence level that the average which would have been obtained by using all the items in the field will be found.

If there are a small number of exceptionally large values among those to be sampled, such as a few accounts for some very large customers, it is desirable that these accounts be grouped separately and either all of these accounts used or a sample which is much larger proportionately. This then becomes a stratified sample. See page 45 for methods of appraising this type of sample. The separation of the exceptionally large values makes the calculation of the sampling variability much less approximate in these cases.

As an illustration, let it be assumed that a sample of 120 observations was drawn from a field of 4,000 in order to estimate the total value of an inventory to establish its reasonableness. Each observation would be a type of inventory item of which there are assumed to be 4,000. It may be assumed that no attempt has been made to stratify the sample since it is known that the inventory items do not differ greatly in value. If there had been a number of exceptionally high value items, these would have been handled separately, and all or a sample of these high values used. It will be assumed that the random number method was used in the selection of the sample.

1. The average value per inventory item was determined from the sample (it is assumed) to be $322.41. Since there were 4,000 inventory items in the field, this would result in an estimate of $1,289,640.00 for the total value of the inventory (4,000 times $322.41).
2. The sample size was assumed to be 120 from a field of 4,000 inventory items.
3. For the purposes of this computation a confidence level of 99% was chosen. This will provide an estimate of sampling reliability which will establish a range such that there are 99 chances out of 100 that the average value which would have been obtained by an average of all 4,000 inventory item values would have been included.
4. The 120 values for the 120 inventory items included in the sample were then grouped into groups of 6 items each in the sequence of their original occurrence in the random number table and the range for each group (difference between highest and lowest value within each group) listed as shown below:

| *Group Number* | *Range* |
|---|---|
| 1 | $150.27 |
| 2 | 100.98 |
| 3 | 50.76 |
| 4 | 540.10 |
| 5 | 201.01 |
| 6 | 89.50 |

| | |
|---|---|
| 7 | 310.00 |
| 8 | 140.50 |
| 9 | 75.00 |
| 10 | 125.10 |
| 11 | 130.45 |
| 12 | 95.90 |
| 13 | 170.00 |
| 14 | 110.10 |
| 15 | 40.00 |
| 16 | 130.00 |
| 17 | 150.26 |
| 18 | 100.10 |
| 19 | 72.29 |
| 20 | 187.50 |
| Average Range | $148.49 |

5. The average range for all of these 20 groups was found to be $148.49.
6. Table 3 gives a factor ($d_2$) of 2.534 for group size 6. Dividing the average range ($148.49) by the factor (2.534) gives an estimate of the standard deviation of $58.60.
7. Table 7 for the column for the 99% confidence level and for field size 4,000 and sample size 100 gives a value of .2544.
8. Multiply the estimate of the standard deviation ($58.60) by the value from Table 7 (.2544),—this gives the sampling reliability of ± $14.91 for the *average* inventory item value.
9. This sampling reliability for the average value per inventory item can be converted to the reliability of the total value by multiplying by the number of inventory items in the field (4,000). This gives a sampling reliability of the *total* inventory value of plus or minus $59,640.
10. It may be concluded, therefore, that there are 99 chances out of 100 that the total inventory is within $59,640 of $1,289,640.

## ESTIMATING THE VALUE OF INFORMATION DERIVED BY FREQUENCY ESTIMATES

Frequently the auditor will wish to evaluate the probable dollar amounts of information derived by frequency estimation. For example, having arrived at an appraisal of the frequency of occurrence of differences in a population sampled and knowing the amounts of the individual differences discovered by him, he may wish to arrive at an estimate of the probable dollar amount of such differences in the entire population.

The obvious way to approach such an evaluation is to convert the whole problem to one of appraisal of variables. Using this technique, the auditor would determine the corrected value of every item sampled by him (as contrasted with the recorded value); he would then on the basis of this information arrive at an estimate of the total true value of the population.

Another method that may be simpler to calculate, particularly where the number of differences is found to be small is the method known as difference estimates.

In this method the estimation of variables is applied to the differences found by the auditor instead of to the corrected balances. This simplifies the calculation where a large number of accounts are determined by the auditor to be accurate and the differences are, consequently, zero.

The differences, under this method, must be listed in the same order as the accounts to which they apply were selected, i.e., in the order in which the random numbers were drawn, not in the order in which they appear in the records. All accounts must be listed using zero as the difference where no difference was found by the auditor.

Then by the methods described in the preceding section, page 40 (i.e. grouping the items and determining the standard deviation by use of the $d_2$ factor), the average value of the differences and the sampling reliability per difference can be calculated. This average and its reliability can be applied to the total number of accounts to arrive at an appraisal of the dollar amount of the effect of the type of differences occurring in the sample.

## DISCOVERY SAMPLING

While the primary objective of discovery sampling is to give reasonable assurance of disclosure in the sample of certain types of events if they occur in the field with some minimum frequency, the auditor may wish an appraisal of the meaning of the sample results when none of these events is disclosed in the sample.

In such an event, the results may be interpreted as in estimation sampling (attributes) when a 0.0% rate of occurrence is found in the sample, making use of Tables 6b and 6c. A detailed discussion on the use of these tables is found on page 39.

# Chapter 6

# STRATIFIED AND CLUSTER SAMPLING

Special methods of sampling may be desirable under certain circumstances in order to reduce the cost of sampling. While various techniques of sampling may be used to achieve increased efficiency in the sampling operation, most of these methods (ratio estimates, multi-stage sampling, etc.) require an advanced knowledge of sampling theory as well as complex computations to determine sample size and reliability.

Two special methods of sampling which may recommend themselves to the accountant, for which computations may be resolved without too much difficulty, are discussed below. These methods involve the use of stratified and cluster sampling.

## STRATIFIED SAMPLING

It is common practice in auditing, when performing a test, to segregate certain accounts or entries, such as those of unusually large amounts, and to check either all these items or a larger proportion of them than for other accounts or entries.

Such a procedure is not only acceptable to the statistician but is looked upon with favor, since the practice serves not only to improve the sample reliability but, by removing exceptionally large values from other sections of the test, renders the determination of the sampling variability more precise.

It may be desired to break up the data to be tested into several groups and to sample in varying degrees each group, perhaps including all the very large accounts, a large proportion of the accounts of moderate size, and a relatively smaller proportion of the smaller accounts.

This method of segregating the data in the field into groups and securing separate random samples for each is termed "stratified sampling" by statisticians.

The tables for determining sample size may be used for *each* group (or strata) separately. However, it may be desired to determine the over-all sampling reliability of a per cent or average from all of the groups combined.

The over-all per cent or average for all groups combined may be obtained by multiplying the *sample* average or per cent for each group by the proportion of items *in the field for that group.* This essentially consists of taking a weighted average of the values obtained as sample estimates for each group, using the relative size of each group in the field as the weight.

The determination of the over-all sampling reliability of the resulting average or per cent is somewhat more complex.

The sampling reliability as determined for an average from Table 7 for each group or strata must be squared (multiplied by itself) and then multiplied by the *square* of the proportion of items *in the field* in that group (strata). The square root of the sum of these products is the sampling reliability of the over-all average or per cent obtained from the stratified sample.

An example of the application of this technique is given below. It is desired to estimate the total value of an inventory by sampling. The stock items are sampled separately by groups (strata) according to the dollar value per item, with the most valuable sampled 100% and the others to a lesser degree. Assume the following situation:

| Total Dollar Value Per Item (Strata) | Number of Stock Items in Strata | Size of Sample Taken | Sample Average Value |
|---|---|---|---|
| Over $1,000 | 100 | 100 | $9,142.27 |
| $100 to $1,000 | 500 | 150 | 513.87 |
| Under $100 | 4,000 | 100 | 46.97 |
| | 4,600 | 350 | |

The average dollar value per inventory item and the total dollar value of the inventory may now be determined as follows:

| Total Dollar Value Per Item (Strata) | Number of Stock Items in Strata | Proportion of Stock Items in Strata | Sample Average Value | Proportion Times Sample Average |
|---|---|---|---|---|
| Over $1,000 | 100 | .02174 | $9,142.27 | $198.7529 |
| $100 to $1,000 | 500 | .10870 | 513.87 | 55.8577 |
| Under $100 | 4,000 | .86956 | 46.97 | 40.8432 |
| | 4,600 | 1.00000 | | $295.4538 |

Estimated average value per item = $295.4538
Estimated total value of inventory 4,600 × $295.4538 = $1,359,087.48

Using the methods outlined for the appraisal of variables samples (see pages 40 to 43, using average ranges, etc.—details not shown here), the following results are attained:

| Total Dollar Value Per Item (Strata) | Number of Stock Items in Strata | Sample Average Value | Reliability of Sample Average * |
|---|---|---|---|
| Over $1,000 | 100 | $9,142.27 | ± 0 |
| $100 to $1,000 | 500 | 513.87 | ±26.78 |
| Under $100 | 4,000 | 46.97 | ± 3.87 |

* Details of calculation not shown here but obtained by methods outlined on pages 40 to 43.

The reliability of the over-all estimate may now be computed as follows:

| Total Dollar Value Per Item (Strata) | Number Stock Items in Strata | Proportion of Total | Reliability of Sample Average | Square of Proportion | Square of Reliability of Average | Product of Squares |
|---|---|---|---|---|---|---|
| Over $1,000 | 100 | .02174 | ± 0 | .000473 | 0 | 0 |
| $100 to $1,000 | 500 | .10870 | ±26.78 | .011816 | 717.17 | 8.4741 |
| Under $100 | 4,000 | .86956 | ± 3.87 | .756135 | 14.98 | 11.3269 |
| | 4,600 | 1.00000 | | | | 19.8010 |

Square root of 19.801 = $4.45
Sampling reliability of over-all average = ± $4.45
Sampling reliability of total estimate = $4.45 × 4,600 = ± $20,470.00

## CLUSTER SAMPLES

The accountant may find it desirable to draw his sample in random "clusters" or groups. As previously defined, a "cluster" sample is obtained by selecting groups of contiguous items or records (sampling units).

To use the following techniques, it will be assumed that all items in the "cluster" are enumerated and that each cluster is *not* subsampled. It is also assumed that each cluster is of the same size and that at least fifty clusters are used.

Percentages of occurrence and averages (or totals) obtained through the use of probability samples of clusters may be appraised for reliability by treating each cluster as though it were the sampling unit rather than the individual items which comprise the cluster.

The methods for appraising sample reliability as outlined for *variables* (see pages 40 to 43) may then be applied to the values obtained from each sample, regardless of the type of data involved (variables or attributes).

Thus, the per cent of occurrence (for attributes) or average value (for variables) for each cluster is treated as though it were a single observation, using the methods previously described for the treatment of variables.

However, since the sampling reliability of an average or total is dependent on the variability of the items in the field from which the sample is drawn, and since the variability of the averages of the clusters is less than the variability of the individual items, the sample size in terms of the number of clusters required will be less than the number of individual observations necessary for unrestricted random sampling for the same reliability. Nevertheless, since a cluster consists of several individual values, the over-all sample size obtained by multiplying the number of clusters by the number of individual observations per cluster will usually be equal to or larger than that necessary for an unrestricted random sample.

Cluster sampling generally results in a lowered reliability for a given number of sample items included than for the comparable size of random sample. As a result, the apparent savings which seem to arise from selecting samples in this manner may well be an illusion, due to the need for a larger sample size to achieve the same result.

# Chapter 7

# AN EXAMPLE OF APPLICATION

The use of the various methods in this book on an attributes problem is illustrated in the example that follows.

A worksheet devised to summarize the application in the auditor's working papers is presented at page 55.

## THE FIELD

The audit step is a circularization of selected customers to obtain confirmation of the balances in their accounts. The client is a manufacturing company selling to approximately 13,000 customers, mostly retail dealers. Individual balances range from very small amounts to high five figures. "Positive" confirmations are used requesting an affirmative confirmation of the balances shown by a statement of account enclosed with the request. A high proportion of replies (over 80%) have been received in the past, but the auditor knows from experience that there are some customers who will not reply, no matter how persuasive or insistent his request might be. As to these, alternative audit procedures will be applied to satisfy the auditor regarding the balances in the accounts. For the purposes of this example it will be assumed that the alternative steps carried out on the somewhat less than 20% "no replies" give the auditor satisfaction equivalent to that derived from the receipt of a signed confirmation. Therefore, the sample will be considered to comprise all requests, not only the replies.

Differences disclosed in individual accounts are considered by the auditor to be of two kinds, "critical" and "noncritical." The auditor, before undertaking the test, has defined critical differences as all differences implying a deliberate falsification or overstatement of the account, a deliberate failure to carry out the normal recording routine, or evidence of misappropriation of a customer's remittance. If any critical differences are found, considerable further investigation will be required to determine their cause, source and possible frequency. This will not be done by sampling, however. While the carrying out of the sampling to its final conclusion is contingent upon no critical errors being found, this, as will be seen, does not preclude the auditor from making an estimate of the probability of there being some that he has not encountered in his sample. Recognizing this, the auditor will select his sample size to give satisfactory precision and confidence level.

Noncritical differences are those arising from normal recording or communication difficulties and may be expected to be encountered in even the best-run organizations. The auditor would, nevertheless, like to perform the most efficient test in terms of minimum effort for desired effect.

## DETERMINATION OF SAMPLE SIZE

It is known from a preliminary survey that there are about 13,000 accounts, and that their aggregate balance as shown by the client-prepared list is approximately $5,436,600. The auditor has decided to circularize all the larger balances and test the smaller ones in order to increase his dollar coverage. After some consideration of the figures, he determines that if all accounts with balances over $5,000 are selected, approximately $1,797,500 or 33.1% of the total will be included and that there will be 151 of these accounts.

The remaining accounts will be sampled. The auditor believes from his experience of previous years that the actual number of accounts expected to have errors in their balances will be less than 5%. He decides that, if this should prove to be so, a 95% assurance that his test results will be within 2% of the true condition of the accounts will be acceptable. This whole procedure of determining where to stratify and how much to sample is an integrated one, the total results being the determinant.

All this information is entered in the worksheet (lines a to f), the 95% assurance and 2% precision being entered in lines e and f alongside (1). The selection of the sample size of 443 is made from Table 2c.

The auditor then for his own additional information would like to know the precision his sample would give him with a 99% confidence level. He turns to Table 2d and finds by interpolation that the sample of 443 will give a reliability of between 2% and 3% (2% would require a sample of 749 and 3% a sample of 342) and he enters this information in lines e and f alongside (2).

Since an evaluation of the probability of undisclosed critical errors will be made from the same sample, the auditor refers to Table 5 where he determines, approximately, that the probabilities of selecting one occurrence in sample range from about 22%, if they exist to the extent of .05% in the field to about 99%, if they exist to the extent of 1%. The exact field and sample sizes do not appear on the Table but use of the next larger field size and interpolation of the sample size gives an approximation of the results (in number of accounts) that can be expected. This information is entered in lines l and m.

Thus having been reassured that the sample size used for frequency estimation of the occurrence of noncritical errors will also give acceptable results if the preconditions regarding critical errors are met, the auditor proceeds with his sampling.

## THE SAMPLE

The accounts are selected by use of random numbers, using Table 1. One hundred fifty-one confirmation requests are sent to the larger customers and 443 are selected randomly from the smaller ones. The audit work then proceeds according to traditional auditing methods.

When the results are in, the auditor proceeds to evaluate his sample. The actual total of the accounts over $5,000 each is determined and subtracted from the grand total, thus permitting the determination of the aggregate and average dollar of the accounts sampled. The auditor's condition that no critical differences be allowed to pass unchallenged has been met. Seven accounts in the sample (excluding for the time being the results of the examinations of the accounts over $5,000), however, have been shown to have balances not entirely accurate. The total amount of the adjustments required to bring these seven accounts to an accurate balance turns out to be $105.00. This information is entered in the worksheet, line k.

## EVALUATION—CRITICAL DIFFERENCES

The auditor, having found no critical differences, still wishes to look into the probability that there may be accounts with critical differences that were not selected for confirmation. The information previously determined from Table 5 has been entered in the worksheet in the section on evaluation of results. Since Table 5 expresses the probability that one *or more* examples would have been found and none was found, he assumes that the probabilities are they exist to a smaller degree than this evaluation indicates.

Alternatively, he could refer to Tables 6b and 6c and find essentially the same information.

## EVALUATION—NONCRITICAL DIFFERENCES

Noncritical differences can be classified into groups for separate calculations, i.e., mispostings, improper cutoffs, etc., but for the purpose of this illustration, only one class of noncritical differences will be assumed to exist. From Table 6 it can be read that a sample of 500 from a field of 15,000 showing a rate of occurrence of 2% (actual sample rate of 1.59%) gives a probability of 95% that the true condition is between 1.1% and 3.5%. Since the actual sample size was 443 the auditor arrives at the figures shown in lines n and o of the worksheet by straight-line interpolation. The auditor then records this in terms of the number of possible differences in the field and enters this information in the worksheet in lines n and o along with similar information using a 99% reliability factor.

The possibility of over 500 accounts (see line o on worksheet) having errors in them, even though noncritical, leads the auditor to inquire into the possible dollar effect of such errors. This he proceeds to calculate using the method described in Chapter 5 as follows:

1. Arrays the errors found in the order in which accounts were selected, treating accounts where no differences were found as errors of zero magnitude.
2. Separates in groups of 7.
3. Determines average range of the groups to be $1.67
4. Using Table 3, determines standard deviation to be $ .62
5. Refers to Table 7 and determines sample reliability for 99% confidence level of (using next higher field size and sample size 400) .1275
6. Determines the product of previous two values to be $ .079
7. Thus the average error per account is ($105 ÷ 443) $.24 ±.08 with a 99% confidence level.
8. Applies this to 12,849 accounts to arrive at amounts shown in worksheets, lines p and q.

Thus, while the auditor is concerned that a large number (up to 552) accounts may have noncritical differences, the relatively insignificant amount of the differences found leads him to conclude that the total effect of errors of this nature is between $2,056 and $4,112 with a 99% confidence level. This does not, of course, include the results of the circularization of the larger accounts which was done 100%.

## CONCLUSION

The process of arriving at a conclusion is a subjective one. The auditor studies the results and considers the relative materiality of the accounts receivable to the total assets. He compares the possible adjustment with the results of operations for the year and with his experience in the previous year. Other factors he may take into consideration are the amount of reserve for allowances and the total assets of the company. After considering all these things together with such subjective factors as steps taken by the client to improve any situation calling for remedial action, the auditor decides whether his test has been satisfactory and whether he should require additional adjustments to the accounts. The statistical portions of his work have been accomplished and he now resumes his traditional auditing procedures, having achieved a better understanding of the precise probabilities and magnitudes of error than would have been possible under traditional methods.

## WORKSHEET FOR EVALUATION OF STATISTICAL SAMPLE FOR ATTRIBUTES

The Field:

| | | | | |
|---|---|---|---|---|
| a. Total universe | items | 13,000 | | $5,436,600 |
| b. Less-Items tested 100% | items | 151 | | 1,797,500 |
| c. Field from which sample was drawn | items | 12,849 | amount | $3,639.100 |

Determination of sample size:

| | | | | |
|---|---|---|---|---|
| d. Assumed maximum rate of noncritical error | | 5% | | |
| e. Desired precision | (1) | 2% | (2) | 3% |
| f. Confidence level | (1) | 95% | (2) | 99% |

Sample:

| | | |
|---|---|---|
| g. Total sample | Items | 443 |
| h. Critical errors found | | (None) |
| Noncritical differences found: | | |
| i. Number of items | | 7 |
| j. Per cent of total sample | | 1.6% |
| k. Amount of differences found | $105.00, per account sampled | $ .24 |

Evaluation of results:

Critical differences

| | | | | |
|---|---|---|---|---|
| l. Probability that one would have been selected | 22%* | 40%* | 92%* | 99%* |
| m. Had they occurred with this frequency (none having been found) | 7(.05%) | 13(.1%) | 65(.5%) | 128(1%) |

| | Reliability of | |
|---|---|---|
| | 95% | 99% |
| Noncritical differences | | |
| Estimated number of accounts with differences— | | |
| n. Lower limits | 128** | 109** |
| o. Upper limits | 475** | 552** |
| Estimated aggregate effect of noncritical differences— | | |
| p. Lower limit | | $2,056 |
| q. Upper limit | | $4,112 |

* Approximated on the basis of sample size 500 and field size 15,000.
** By interpolation for sample size 443.

# BIBLIOGRAPHY

## BOOKS

American Institute of Certified Public Accountants. "Glossary of Statistical Terms and Bibliography on the Application of Statistical Methods to Accounting, Auditing and Management Control." New York, 1958.

Arkin, H. *Handbook of Sampling in Auditing and Accounting,* New York: McGraw-Hill Book Co., 1962.

Arkin, H., and Colton, R. R. *Outline of Statistical Methods,* 4th rev. ed., New York: Barnes and Noble, Inc., 1956.

McCarthy, Philip J. "Sampling, Elementary Principles," Bulletin No. 15. Ithaca, N.Y.: Cornell University, (pamphlet free to New York residents; 25 cents to others).

Trueblood, Robert M., and Cyert, R. M. *Sampling Techniques in Accounting,* Englewood Cliffs, N.J.: Prentice-Hall, Inc., 1957.

Vance, Lawrence L., and Neter, John. *Statistical Sampling for Auditors and Accountants,* New York: John Wiley & Sons, Inc., 1956.

## TABLES OF RANDOM DIGITS

Interstate Commerce Commission. *Table of 105,000 Random Decimal Digits,* Washington, D.C.: Bureau of Transport Economics and Statistics, 1949.

Kendall, M. G., and Smith, B. B. *Tables of Random Sampling Numbers,* Tracts for Computers XXIV. London: Cambridge University Press, 1939.

Rand Corporation. *A Million Random Digits,* Glencoe, Ill.: The Free Press, 1955.

# TABLE 1 *Table of Random Digits*

| Line \ Col. | (1) | (2) | (3) | (4) | (5) | (6) | (7) | (8) | (9) | (10) | (11) | (12) | (13) | (14) |
|---|---|---|---|---|---|---|---|---|---|---|---|---|---|---|
| 1 | 10480 | 15011 | 01536 | 02011 | 81647 | 91646 | 69179 | 14194 | 62590 | 36207 | 20969 | 99570 | 91291 | 90700 |
| 2 | 22368 | 46573 | 25595 | 85393 | 30995 | 89198 | 27982 | 53402 | 93965 | 34095 | 52666 | 19174 | 39615 | 99505 |
| 3 | 24130 | 48360 | 22527 | 97265 | 76393 | 64809 | 15179 | 24830 | 49340 | 32081 | 30680 | 19655 | 63348 | 58629 |
| 4 | 42167 | 93093 | 06243 | 61680 | 07856 | 16376 | 39440 | 53537 | 71341 | 57004 | 00849 | 74917 | 97758 | 16379 |
| 5 | 37570 | 39975 | 81837 | 16656 | 06121 | 91782 | 60468 | 81305 | 49684 | 60672 | 14110 | 06927 | 01263 | 54613 |
| 6 | 77921 | 06907 | 11008 | 42751 | 27756 | 53498 | 18602 | 70659 | 90655 | 15053 | 21916 | 81825 | 44394 | 42880 |
| 7 | 99562 | 72905 | 56420 | 69994 | 98872 | 31016 | 71194 | 18738 | 44013 | 48840 | 63213 | 21069 | 10634 | 12952 |
| 8 | 96301 | 91977 | 05463 | 07972 | 18876 | 20922 | 94595 | 56869 | 69014 | 60045 | 18425 | 84903 | 42508 | 32307 |
| 9 | 89579 | 14342 | 63661 | 10281 | 17453 | 18103 | 57740 | 84378 | 25331 | 12566 | 58678 | 44947 | 05585 | 56941 |
| 10 | 85475 | 36857 | 53342 | 53988 | 53060 | 59533 | 38867 | 62300 | 08158 | 17983 | 16439 | 11458 | 18593 | 64952 |
| 11 | 28918 | 69578 | 88231 | 33276 | 70997 | 79936 | 56865 | 05859 | 90106 | 31595 | 01547 | 85590 | 91610 | 78188 |
| 12 | 63553 | 40961 | 48235 | 03427 | 49626 | 69445 | 18663 | 72695 | 52180 | 20847 | 12234 | 90511 | 33703 | 90322 |
| 13 | 09429 | 93969 | 52636 | 92737 | 88974 | 33488 | 36320 | 17617 | 30015 | 08272 | 84115 | 27156 | 30613 | 74952 |
| 14 | 10365 | 61129 | 87529 | 85689 | 48237 | 52267 | 67689 | 93394 | 01511 | 26358 | 85104 | 20285 | 29975 | 89868 |
| 15 | 07119 | 97336 | 71048 | 08178 | 77233 | 13916 | 47564 | 81056 | 97735 | 85977 | 29372 | 74461 | 28551 | 90707 |
| 16 | 51085 | 12765 | 51821 | 51259 | 77452 | 16308 | 60756 | 92144 | 49442 | 53900 | 70960 | 63990 | 75601 | 40719 |
| 17 | 02368 | 21382 | 52404 | 60268 | 89368 | 19885 | 55322 | 44819 | 01188 | 65255 | 64835 | 44919 | 05944 | 55157 |
| 18 | 01011 | 54092 | 33362 | 94904 | 31273 | 04146 | 18594 | 29852 | 71585 | 85030 | 51132 | 01915 | 92747 | 64951 |
| 19 | 52162 | 53916 | 46369 | 58586 | 23216 | 14513 | 83149 | 98736 | 23495 | 64350 | 94738 | 17752 | 35156 | 35749 |
| 20 | 07056 | 97628 | 33787 | 09998 | 42698 | 06691 | 76988 | 13602 | 51851 | 46104 | 88916 | 19509 | 25625 | 58104 |
| 21 | 48663 | 91245 | 85828 | 14346 | 09172 | 30168 | 90229 | 04734 | 59193 | 22178 | 30421 | 61666 | 99904 | 32812 |
| 22 | 54164 | 58492 | 22421 | 74103 | 47070 | 25306 | 76468 | 26384 | 58151 | 06646 | 21524 | 15227 | 96909 | 44592 |
| 23 | 32639 | 32363 | 05597 | 24200 | 13363 | 38005 | 94342 | 28728 | 35806 | 06912 | 17012 | 64161 | 18296 | 22851 |
| 24 | 29334 | 27001 | 87637 | 87308 | 58731 | 00256 | 45834 | 15398 | 46557 | 41135 | 10367 | 07684 | 36188 | 18510 |
| 25 | 02488 | 33062 | 28834 | 07351 | 19731 | 92420 | 60952 | 61280 | 50001 | 67658 | 32586 | 86679 | 50720 | 94953 |
| 26 | 81525 | 72295 | 04839 | 96423 | 24878 | 82651 | 66566 | 14778 | 76797 | 14780 | 13300 | 87074 | 79666 | 95725 |
| 27 | 29676 | 20591 | 68086 | 26432 | 46901 | 20849 | 89768 | 81536 | 86645 | 12659 | 92259 | 57102 | 80428 | 25280 |
| 28 | 00742 | 57392 | 39064 | 66432 | 84673 | 40027 | 32832 | 61362 | 98947 | 96067 | 64760 | 64584 | 96096 | 98253 |
| 29 | 05366 | 04213 | 25669 | 26422 | 44407 | 44048 | 37937 | 63904 | 45766 | 66134 | 75470 | 66520 | 34693 | 90449 |
| 30 | 91921 | 26418 | 64117 | 94305 | 26766 | 25940 | 39972 | 22209 | 71500 | 64568 | 91402 | 42416 | 07844 | 69618 |
| 31 | 00582 | 04711 | 87917 | 77341 | 42206 | 35126 | 74087 | 99547 | 81817 | 42607 | 43808 | 76655 | 62028 | 76630 |
| 32 | 00725 | 69884 | 62797 | 56170 | 86324 | 88072 | 76222 | 36086 | 84637 | 93161 | 76038 | 65855 | 77919 | 88006 |
| 33 | 69011 | 65795 | 95876 | 55293 | 18988 | 27354 | 26575 | 08625 | 40801 | 59920 | 29841 | 80150 | 12777 | 48501 |
| 34 | 25976 | 57948 | 29888 | 88604 | 67917 | 48708 | 18912 | 82271 | 65424 | 69774 | 33611 | 54262 | 85963 | 03547 |
| 35 | 09763 | 83473 | 73577 | 12908 | 30883 | 18317 | 28290 | 35797 | 05998 | 41688 | 34952 | 37888 | 38917 | 88050 |
| 36 | 91567 | 42595 | 27958 | 30134 | 04024 | 86385 | 29880 | 99730 | 55536 | 84855 | 29080 | 09250 | 79656 | 73211 |
| 37 | 17955 | 56349 | 90999 | 49127 | 20044 | 59931 | 06115 | 20542 | 18059 | 02008 | 73708 | 83517 | 36103 | 42791 |
| 38 | 46503 | 18584 | 18845 | 49618 | 02304 | 51038 | 20655 | 58727 | 28168 | 15475 | 56942 | 53389 | 20562 | 87338 |
| 39 | 92157 | 89634 | 94824 | 78171 | 84610 | 82834 | 09922 | 25417 | 44137 | 48413 | 25555 | 21246 | 35509 | 20468 |
| 40 | 14577 | 62765 | 35605 | 81263 | 39667 | 47358 | 56873 | 56307 | 61607 | 49518 | 89656 | 20103 | 77490 | 18062 |
| 41 | 98427 | 07523 | 33362 | 64270 | 01638 | 92477 | 66969 | 98420 | 04880 | 45585 | 46565 | 04102 | 46880 | 45709 |
| 42 | 34914 | 63976 | 88720 | 82765 | 34476 | 17032 | 87589 | 40836 | 32427 | 70002 | 70663 | 88863 | 77775 | 69348 |
| 43 | 70060 | 28277 | 39475 | 46473 | 23219 | 53416 | 94970 | 25832 | 69975 | 94884 | 19661 | 72828 | 00102 | 66794 |
| 44 | 53976 | 54914 | 06990 | 67245 | 68350 | 82948 | 11398 | 42878 | 80287 | 88267 | 47363 | 46634 | 06541 | 97809 |
| 45 | 76072 | 29515 | 40980 | 07391 | 58745 | 25774 | 22987 | 80059 | 39911 | 96189 | 41151 | 14222 | 60697 | 59583 |
| 46 | 90725 | 52210 | 83974 | 29992 | 65831 | 38857 | 50490 | 83765 | 55657 | 14361 | 31720 | 57375 | 56228 | 41546 |
| 47 | 64364 | 67412 | 33339 | 31926 | 14883 | 24413 | 59744 | 92351 | 97473 | 89286 | 35931 | 04110 | 23726 | 51900 |
| 48 | 08962 | 00358 | 31662 | 25388 | 61642 | 34072 | 81249 | 35648 | 56891 | 69352 | 48373 | 45578 | 78547 | 81788 |
| 49 | 95012 | 68379 | 93526 | 70765 | 10592 | 04542 | 76463 | 54328 | 02349 | 17247 | 28865 | 14777 | 62730 | 92277 |
| 50 | 15664 | 10493 | 20492 | 38391 | 91132 | 21999 | 59516 | 81652 | 27195 | 48223 | 46751 | 22923 | 32261 | 85653 |

From *Table of 105,000 Random Decimal Digits,*
Interstate Commerce Commission Bureau of Transport Economics and Statistics.

**TABLE 1**

| Line \ Col. | (1) | (2) | (3) | (4) | (5) | (6) | (7) | (8) | (9) | (10) | (11) | (12) | (13) | (14) |
|---|---|---|---|---|---|---|---|---|---|---|---|---|---|---|
| 51 | 16408 | 81899 | 04153 | 53381 | 79401 | 21438 | 83035 | 92350 | 36693 | 31238 | 59649 | 91754 | 72772 | 02338 |
| 52 | 18629 | 81953 | 05520 | 91962 | 04739 | 13092 | 97662 | 24822 | 94730 | 06496 | 35090 | 04822 | 86774 | 98289 |
| 53 | 73115 | 35101 | 47498 | 87637 | 99016 | 71060 | 88824 | 71013 | 18735 | 20286 | 23153 | 72924 | 35165 | 43040 |
| 54 | 57491 | 16703 | 23167 | 49323 | 45021 | 33132 | 12544 | 41035 | 80780 | 45393 | 44812 | 12515 | 98931 | 91202 |
| 55 | 30405 | 83946 | 23792 | 14422 | 15059 | 45799 | 22716 | 19792 | 09983 | 74353 | 68668 | 30429 | 70735 | 25499 |
| 56 | 16631 | 35006 | 85900 | 98275 | 32388 | 52390 | 16815 | 69298 | 82732 | 38480 | 73817 | 32523 | 41961 | 44437 |
| 57 | 96773 | 20206 | 42559 | 78985 | 05300 | 22164 | 24369 | 54224 | 35083 | 19687 | 11052 | 91491 | 60383 | 19746 |
| 58 | 38935 | 64202 | 14349 | 82674 | 66523 | 44133 | 00697 | 35552 | 35970 | 19124 | 63318 | 29686 | 03387 | 59846 |
| 59 | 31624 | 76384 | 17403 | 53363 | 44167 | 64486 | 64758 | 75366 | 76554 | 31601 | 12614 | 33072 | 60332 | 92325 |
| 60 | 78919 | 19474 | 23632 | 27889 | 47914 | 02584 | 37680 | 20801 | 72152 | 39339 | 34806 | 08930 | 85001 | 87820 |
| 61 | 03931 | 33309 | 57047 | 74211 | 63445 | 17361 | 62825 | 39908 | 05607 | 91284 | 68833 | 25570 | 38818 | 46920 |
| 62 | 74426 | 33278 | 43972 | 10119 | 89917 | 15665 | 52872 | 73823 | 73144 | 88662 | 88970 | 74492 | 51805 | 99378 |
| 63 | 09066 | 00903 | 20795 | 95452 | 92648 | 45454 | 09552 | 88815 | 16553 | 51125 | 79375 | 97596 | 16296 | 66092 |
| 64 | 42238 | 12426 | 87025 | 14267 | 20979 | 04508 | 64535 | 31355 | 86064 | 29472 | 47689 | 05974 | 52468 | 16834 |
| 65 | 16153 | 08002 | 26504 | 41744 | 81959 | 65642 | 74240 | 56302 | 00033 | 67107 | 77510 | 70625 | 28725 | 34191 |
| 66 | 21457 | 40742 | 29820 | 96783 | 29400 | 21840 | 15035 | 34537 | 33310 | 06116 | 95240 | 15957 | 16572 | 06004 |
| 67 | 21581 | 57802 | 02050 | 89728 | 17937 | 37621 | 47075 | 42080 | 97403 | 48626 | 68995 | 43805 | 33386 | 21597 |
| 68 | 55612 | 78095 | 83197 | 33732 | 05810 | 24813 | 86902 | 60397 | 16489 | 03264 | 88525 | 42786 | 05269 | 92532 |
| 69 | 44657 | 66999 | 99324 | 51281 | 84463 | 60563 | 79312 | 93454 | 68876 | 25471 | 93911 | 25650 | 12682 | 73572 |
| 70 | 91340 | 84979 | 46949 | 81973 | 37949 | 61023 | 43997 | 15263 | 80644 | 43942 | 89203 | 71795 | 99533 | 50501 |
| 71 | 91227 | 21199 | 31935 | 27022 | 84067 | 05462 | 35216 | 14486 | 29891 | 68607 | 41867 | 14951 | 91696 | 85065 |
| 72 | 50001 | 38140 | 66321 | 19924 | 72163 | 09538 | 12151 | 06878 | 91903 | 18749 | 34405 | 56087 | 82790 | 70925 |
| 73 | 65390 | 05224 | 72958 | 28609 | 81406 | 39147 | 25549 | 48542 | 42627 | 45233 | 57202 | 94617 | 23772 | 07896 |
| 74 | 27504 | 96131 | 83944 | 41575 | 10573 | 08619 | 64482 | 73923 | 36152 | 05184 | 94142 | 25299 | 84387 | 34925 |
| 75 | 37169 | 94851 | 39117 | 89632 | 00959 | 16487 | 65536 | 49071 | 39782 | 17095 | 02330 | 74301 | 00275 | 48280 |
| 76 | 11508 | 70225 | 51111 | 38351 | 19444 | 66499 | 71945 | 05422 | 13442 | 78675 | 84081 | 66938 | 93654 | 59894 |
| 77 | 37449 | 30362 | 06694 | 54690 | 04052 | 53115 | 62757 | 95348 | 78662 | 11163 | 81651 | 50245 | 34971 | 52924 |
| 78 | 46515 | 70331 | 85922 | 38329 | 57015 | 15765 | 97161 | 17869 | 45349 | 61796 | 66345 | 81073 | 49106 | 79860 |
| 79 | 30986 | 81223 | 42416 | 58353 | 21532 | 30502 | 32305 | 86482 | 05174 | 07901 | 54339 | 58861 | 74818 | 46942 |
| 80 | 63798 | 64995 | 46583 | 09785 | 44160 | 78128 | 83991 | 42865 | 92520 | 83531 | 80377 | 35909 | 81250 | 54238 |
| 81 | 82486 | 84846 | 99254 | 67632 | 43218 | 50076 | 21361 | 64816 | 51202 | 88124 | 41870 | 52689 | 51275 | 83556 |
| 82 | 21885 | 32906 | 92431 | 09060 | 64297 | 51674 | 64126 | 62570 | 26123 | 05155 | 59194 | 52799 | 28225 | 85762 |
| 83 | 60336 | 98782 | 07408 | 53458 | 13564 | 59089 | 26445 | 29789 | 85205 | 41001 | 12535 | 12133 | 14645 | 23541 |
| 84 | 43937 | 46891 | 24010 | 25560 | 86355 | 33941 | 25786 | 54990 | 71899 | 15475 | 95434 | 98227 | 21824 | 19585 |
| 85 | 97656 | 63175 | 89303 | 16275 | 07100 | 92063 | 21942 | 18611 | 47348 | 20203 | 18534 | 03862 | 78095 | 50136 |
| 86 | 03299 | 01221 | 05418 | 38982 | 55758 | 92237 | 26759 | 86367 | 21216 | 98442 | 08303 | 56613 | 91511 | 75928 |
| 87 | 79626 | 06486 | 03574 | 17668 | 07785 | 76020 | 79924 | 25651 | 83325 | 88428 | 85076 | 72811 | 22717 | 50585 |
| 88 | 85636 | 68335 | 47539 | 03129 | 65651 | 11977 | 02510 | 26113 | 99447 | 68645 | 34327 | 15152 | 55230 | 93448 |
| 89 | 18039 | 14367 | 61337 | 06177 | 12143 | 46609 | 32989 | 74014 | 64708 | 00533 | 35398 | 58408 | 13261 | 47908 |
| 90 | 08362 | 15656 | 60627 | 36478 | 65648 | 16764 | 53412 | 09013 | 07832 | 41574 | 17639 | 82163 | 60859 | 75567 |
| 91 | 79556 | 29068 | 04142 | 16268 | 15387 | 12856 | 66227 | 38358 | 22478 | 73373 | 88732 | 09443 | 82558 | 05250 |
| 92 | 92608 | 82674 | 27072 | 32534 | 17075 | 27698 | 98204 | 63863 | 11951 | 34648 | 88022 | 56148 | 34925 | 57031 |
| 93 | 23982 | 25835 | 40055 | 67006 | 12293 | 02753 | 14827 | 23235 | 35071 | 99704 | 37543 | 11601 | 35503 | 85171 |
| 94 | 09915 | 96306 | 05908 | 97901 | 28395 | 14186 | 00821 | 80703 | 70426 | 75647 | 76310 | 88717 | 37890 | 40129 |
| 95 | 59037 | 33300 | 26695 | 62247 | 69927 | 76123 | 50842 | 43834 | 86654 | 70959 | 79725 | 93872 | 28117 | 19233 |
| 96 | 42488 | 78077 | 69882 | 61657 | 34136 | 79180 | 97526 | 43092 | 04098 | 73571 | 80799 | 76536 | 71255 | 64239 |
| 97 | 46764 | 86273 | 63003 | 93017 | 31204 | 36692 | 40202 | 35275 | 57306 | 55543 | 53203 | 16098 | 47625 | 88684 |
| 98 | 03237 | 45430 | 55417 | 63282 | 90816 | 17349 | 88298 | 90183 | 36600 | 78406 | 06216 | 95787 | 42579 | 90730 |
| 99 | 86591 | 81482 | 52667 | 61582 | 14972 | 90053 | 89534 | 76036 | 49199 | 43716 | 97548 | 04379 | 46370 | 28672 |
| 100 | 38534 | 01715 | 94964 | 87288 | 65680 | 43772 | 39560 | 12918 | 86537 | 62738 | 19636 | 51132 | 25739 | 56947 |

## TABLE 1

| Line / Col. | (1) | (2) | (3) | (4) | (5) | (6) | (7) | (8) | (9) | (10) | (11) | (12) | (13) | (14) |
|---|---|---|---|---|---|---|---|---|---|---|---|---|---|---|
| 101 | 13284 | 16834 | 74151 | 92027 | 24670 | 36665 | 00770 | 22878 | 02179 | 51602 | 07270 | 76517 | 97275 | 45960 |
| 102 | 21224 | 00370 | 30420 | 03883 | 94648 | 89428 | 41583 | 17564 | 27395 | 63904 | 41548 | 49197 | 82277 | 24120 |
| 103 | 99052 | 47887 | 81085 | 64933 | 66279 | 80432 | 65793 | 83287 | 34142 | 13241 | 30590 | 97760 | 35848 | 91983 |
| 104 | 00199 | 50993 | 98603 | 38452 | 87890 | 94624 | 69721 | 57484 | 67501 | 77638 | 44331 | 11257 | 71131 | 11059 |
| 105 | 60578 | 06483 | 28733 | 37867 | 07936 | 98710 | 98539 | 27186 | 31237 | 80612 | 44488 | 97819 | 70401 | 95419 |
| 106 | 91240 | 18312 | 17441 | 01929 | 18163 | 69201 | 31211 | 54288 | 39296 | 37318 | 65724 | 90401 | 79017 | 62077 |
| 107 | 97458 | 14229 | 12063 | 59611 | 32249 | 90466 | 33216 | 19358 | 02591 | 54263 | 88449 | 01912 | 07436 | 50813 |
| 108 | 35249 | 38646 | 34475 | 72417 | 60514 | 69257 | 12489 | 51924 | 86871 | 92446 | 36607 | 11458 | 30440 | 52639 |
| 109 | 38980 | 46600 | 11759 | 11900 | 46743 | 27860 | 77940 | 39298 | 97838 | 95145 | 32378 | 68038 | 89351 | 37005 |
| 110 | 10750 | 52745 | 38749 | 87365 | 58959 | 53731 | 89295 | 59062 | 39404 | 13198 | 59960 | 70408 | 29812 | 83126 |
| 111 | 36247 | 27850 | 73958 | 20673 | 37800 | 63835 | 71051 | 84724 | 52492 | 22342 | 78071 | 17456 | 96104 | 18327 |
| 112 | 70994 | 66986 | 99744 | 72438 | 01174 | 42159 | 11392 | 20724 | 54322 | 36923 | 70009 | 23233 | 65438 | 59685 |
| 113 | 99638 | 94702 | 11463 | 18148 | 81386 | 80431 | 90628 | 52506 | 02016 | 85151 | 88598 | 47821 | 00265 | 82525 |
| 114 | 72055 | 15774 | 43857 | 99805 | 10419 | 76939 | 25993 | 03544 | 21560 | 83471 | 43989 | 90770 | 22965 | 44247 |
| 115 | 24038 | 65541 | 85788 | 55835 | 38835 | 59399 | 13790 | 35112 | 01324 | 39520 | 76210 | 22467 | 83275 | 32286 |
| 116 | 74976 | 14631 | 35908 | 28221 | 39470 | 91548 | 12854 | 30166 | 09073 | 75887 | 36782 | 00268 | 97121 | 57676 |
| 117 | 35553 | 71628 | 70189 | 26436 | 63407 | 91178 | 90348 | 55359 | 80392 | 41012 | 36270 | 77786 | 89578 | 21059 |
| 118 | 35676 | 12797 | 51434 | 82976 | 42010 | 26344 | 92920 | 92155 | 58807 | 54644 | 58581 | 95331 | 78629 | 73344 |
| 119 | 74815 | 67523 | 72985 | 23183 | 02446 | 63594 | 98924 | 20633 | 58842 | 85961 | 07648 | 70164 | 34994 | 67662 |
| 120 | 45246 | 88048 | 65173 | 50989 | 91060 | 89894 | 36036 | 32819 | 68559 | 99221 | 49475 | 50558 | 34698 | 71800 |
| 121 | 76509 | 47069 | 86378 | 41797 | 11910 | 49672 | 88575 | 97966 | 32466 | 10083 | 54728 | 81972 | 58975 | 30761 |
| 122 | 19689 | 90332 | 04315 | 21358 | 97248 | 11188 | 39062 | 63312 | 52496 | 07349 | 79178 | 33692 | 57352 | 72862 |
| 123 | 42751 | 35318 | 97513 | 61537 | 54955 | 08159 | 00337 | 80778 | 27507 | 95478 | 21252 | 12746 | 37554 | 97775 |
| 124 | 11946 | 22681 | 45045 | 13964 | 57517 | 59419 | 58045 | 44067 | 58716 | 58840 | 45557 | 96345 | 33271 | 53464 |
| 125 | 96518 | 48688 | 20996 | 11090 | 48396 | 57177 | 83867 | 86464 | 14342 | 21545 | 46717 | 72364 | 86954 | 55580 |
| 126 | 35726 | 58643 | 76869 | 84622 | 39098 | 36083 | 72505 | 92265 | 23107 | 60278 | 05822 | 46760 | 44294 | 07672 |
| 127 | 39737 | 42750 | 48968 | 70536 | 84864 | 64952 | 38404 | 94317 | 65402 | 13589 | 01055 | 79044 | 19308 | 83623 |
| 128 | 97025 | 66492 | 56177 | 04049 | 80312 | 48028 | 26408 | 43591 | 75528 | 65341 | 49044 | 95495 | 81256 | 53214 |
| 129 | 62814 | 08075 | 09788 | 56350 | 76787 | 51591 | 54509 | 49295 | 85830 | 59860 | 30883 | 89660 | 96142 | 18354 |
| 130 | 25578 | 22950 | 15227 | 83291 | 41737 | 79599 | 96191 | 71845 | 86899 | 70694 | 24290 | 01551 | 80092 | 82118 |
| 131 | 68763 | 69576 | 88991 | 49662 | 46704 | 63362 | 56625 | 00481 | 73323 | 91427 | 15264 | 06969 | 57048 | 54149 |
| 132 | 17900 | 00813 | 64361 | 60725 | 88974 | 61005 | 99709 | 30666 | 26451 | 11528 | 44323 | 34778 | 60342 | 60388 |
| 133 | 71944 | 60227 | 63551 | 71109 | 05624 | 43836 | 58254 | 26160 | 32116 | 63403 | 35404 | 57146 | 10909 | 07346 |
| 134 | 54684 | 93691 | 85132 | 64399 | 29182 | 44324 | 14491 | 55226 | 78793 | 34107 | 30374 | 48429 | 51376 | 09559 |
| 135 | 25946 | 27623 | 11258 | 65204 | 52832 | 50880 | 22273 | 05554 | 99521 | 73791 | 85744 | 29276 | 70326 | 60251 |
| 136 | 01353 | 39318 | 44961 | 44972 | 91766 | 90262 | 56073 | 06606 | 51826 | 18893 | 83448 | 31915 | 97764 | 75091 |
| 137 | 99083 | 88191 | 27662 | 99113 | 57174 | 35571 | 99884 | 13951 | 71057 | 53961 | 61448 | 74909 | 07322 | 80960 |
| 138 | 52021 | 45406 | 37945 | 75234 | 24327 | 86978 | 22644 | 87779 | 23753 | 99926 | 63898 | 54886 | 18051 | 96314 |
| 139 | 78755 | 47744 | 43776 | 83098 | 03225 | 14281 | 83637 | 55984 | 13300 | 52212 | 58781 | 14905 | 46502 | 04472 |
| 140 | 25282 | 69106 | 59180 | 16257 | 22810 | 43609 | 12224 | 25643 | 89884 | 31149 | 85423 | 32581 | 34374 | 70873 |
| 141 | 11959 | 94202 | 02743 | 86847 | 79725 | 51811 | 12998 | 76844 | 05320 | 54236 | 53891 | 70226 | 38632 | 84776 |
| 142 | 11644 | 13792 | 98190 | 01424 | 30078 | 28197 | 55583 | 05197 | 47714 | 68440 | 22016 | 79204 | 06862 | 94451 |
| 143 | 06307 | 97912 | 68110 | 59812 | 95448 | 43244 | 31262 | 88880 | 13040 | 16458 | 43813 | 89416 | 42482 | 33939 |
| 144 | 76285 | 75714 | 89585 | 99296 | 52640 | 46518 | 55486 | 90754 | 88932 | 19937 | 57119 | 23251 | 55619 | 23679 |
| 145 | 55322 | 07598 | 39600 | 60866 | 63007 | 20007 | 66819 | 84164 | 61131 | 81429 | 60676 | 42807 | 78286 | 29015 |
| 146 | 78017 | 90928 | 90220 | 92503 | 83375 | 26986 | 74399 | 30885 | 88567 | 29169 | 72816 | 53357 | 15428 | 86932 |
| 147 | 44768 | 43342 | 20696 | 26331 | 43140 | 69744 | 82928 | 24988 | 94237 | 46138 | 77426 | 39039 | 55596 | 12655 |
| 148 | 25100 | 19336 | 14605 | 86603 | 51680 | 97678 | 24261 | 02464 | 86563 | 74812 | 60069 | 71674 | 15478 | 47642 |
| 149 | 83612 | 46623 | 62876 | 85197 | 07824 | 91392 | 58317 | 37726 | 84628 | 42221 | 10268 | 20692 | 15699 | 29167 |
| 150 | 41347 | 81666 | 82961 | 60413 | 71020 | 83658 | 02410 | 33322 | 66036 | 98712 | 46795 | 16308 | 28413 | 05417 |

| Line \ Col. | (1) | (2) | (3) | (4) | (5) | (6) | (7) | (8) | (9) | (10) | (11) | (12) | (13) | (14) |
|---|---|---|---|---|---|---|---|---|---|---|---|---|---|---|
| 151 | 38128 | 51178 | 75096 | 13609 | 16110 | 73533 | 42564 | 59870 | 29399 | 67834 | 91055 | 89917 | 51096 | 89011 |
| 152 | 60950 | 00455 | 73254 | 96067 | 50717 | 13878 | 03216 | 78274 | 65863 | 37011 | 91283 | 33914 | 91303 | 49326 |
| 153 | 90524 | 17320 | 29832 | 96118 | 75792 | 25326 | 22940 | 24904 | 80523 | 38928 | 91374 | 55597 | 97567 | 38914 |
| 154 | 49897 | 18278 | 67160 | 39408 | 97056 | 43517 | 84426 | 59650 | 20247 | 19293 | 02019 | 14790 | 02852 | 05819 |
| 155 | 18494 | 99209 | 81060 | 19488 | 65596 | 59787 | 47939 | 91225 | 98768 | 43688 | 00438 | 05548 | 09443 | 82897 |
| 156 | 65373 | 72984 | 30171 | 37741 | 70203 | 94094 | 87261 | 30056 | 58124 | 70133 | 18936 | 02138 | 59372 | 09075 |
| 157 | 40653 | 12843 | 04213 | 70925 | 95360 | 55774 | 76439 | 61768 | 52817 | 81151 | 52188 | 31940 | 54273 | 49032 |
| 158 | 51638 | 22238 | 56344 | 44587 | 83231 | 50317 | 74541 | 07719 | 25472 | 41602 | 77318 | 15145 | 57515 | 07633 |
| 159 | 69742 | 99303 | 62578 | 83575 | 30337 | 07488 | 51941 | 84316 | 42067 | 49692 | 28616 | 29101 | 03013 | 73449 |
| 160 | 58012 | 74072 | 67488 | 74580 | 47992 | 69482 | 58624 | 17106 | 47538 | 13452 | 22620 | 24260 | 40155 | 74716 |
| 161 | 18348 | 19855 | 42887 | 08279 | 43206 | 47077 | 42637 | 45606 | 00011 | 20662 | 14642 | 49984 | 94509 | 56380 |
| 162 | 59614 | 09193 | 58064 | 29086 | 44385 | 45740 | 70752 | 05663 | 49081 | 26960 | 57454 | 99264 | 24142 | 74648 |
| 163 | 75688 | 28630 | 39210 | 52897 | 62748 | 72658 | 98059 | 67202 | 72789 | 01869 | 13496 | 14663 | 87645 | 89713 |
| 164 | 13941 | 77802 | 69101 | 70061 | 35460 | 34576 | 15412 | 81304 | 58757 | 35498 | 94830 | 75581 | 00603 | 97701 |
| 165 | 96656 | 86420 | 96475 | 86458 | 54463 | 96419 | 55417 | 41375 | 76886 | 19008 | 66877 | 35934 | 59801 | 00497 |
| 166 | 03363 | 82042 | 15942 | 14549 | 38324 | 87094 | 19069 | 67590 | 11087 | 68570 | 22591 | 65232 | 85915 | 91499 |
| 167 | 70366 | 08390 | 69155 | 25496 | 13240 | 57407 | 91407 | 49160 | 07379 | 34444 | 94567 | 66035 | 38918 | 65708 |
| 168 | 47870 | 36605 | 12927 | 16043 | 53257 | 93796 | 52721 | 73120 | 48025 | 76074 | 95605 | 67422 | 41646 | 14557 |
| 169 | 79504 | 77606 | 22761 | 30518 | 28373 | 73898 | 30550 | 76684 | 77366 | 32276 | 04690 | 61667 | 64798 | 66276 |
| 170 | 46967 | 74841 | 50923 | 15339 | 37755 | 98995 | 40162 | 89561 | 69199 | 42257 | 11647 | 47603 | 48779 | 97907 |
| 171 | 14558 | 50769 | 35444 | 59030 | 87516 | 48193 | 02945 | 00922 | 48189 | 04724 | 21263 | 20892 | 92955 | 90251 |
| 172 | 12440 | 25057 | 01138 | 38611 | 28135 | 68089 | 10954 | 10097 | 54243 | 06460 | 50856 | 65435 | 79377 | 53890 |
| 173 | 32293 | 29938 | 68653 | 10497 | 98919 | 46587 | 77701 | 99119 | 93165 | 67788 | 17638 | 23097 | 21468 | 36992 |
| 174 | 10640 | 21875 | 72462 | 77981 | 56550 | 55999 | 87310 | 69643 | 45124 | 00349 | 25748 | 00844 | 96831 | 30651 |
| 175 | 47615 | 23169 | 39571 | 56972 | 20628 | 21788 | 51736 | 33133 | 72696 | 32605 | 41569 | 76148 | 91544 | 21121 |
| 176 | 16948 | 11128 | 71624 | 72754 | 49084 | 96303 | 27830 | 45817 | 67867 | 18062 | 87453 | 17226 | 72904 | 71474 |
| 177 | 21258 | 61092 | 66634 | 70335 | 92448 | 17354 | 83432 | 49608 | 66520 | 06442 | 59664 | 20420 | 39201 | 69549 |
| 178 | 15072 | 48853 | 15178 | 30730 | 47481 | 48490 | 41436 | 25015 | 49932 | 20474 | 53821 | 51015 | 79841 | 32405 |
| 179 | 99154 | 57412 | 09858 | 65671 | 70655 | 71479 | 63520 | 31357 | 56968 | 06729 | 34465 | 70685 | 04184 | 25250 |
| 180 | 08759 | 61089 | 23706 | 32994 | 35426 | 36666 | 63988 | 98844 | 37533 | 08269 | 27021 | 45886 | 22835 | 78451 |
| 181 | 67323 | 57839 | 61114 | 62192 | 47547 | 58023 | 64630 | 34886 | 98777 | 75442 | 95592 | 06141 | 45096 | 73117 |
| 182 | 09255 | 13986 | 84834 | 20764 | 72206 | 89393 | 34548 | 93438 | 88730 | 61805 | 78955 | 18952 | 46436 | 58740 |
| 183 | 36304 | 74712 | 00374 | 10107 | 85061 | 69228 | 81969 | 92216 | 03568 | 39630 | 81869 | 52824 | 50937 | 27954 |
| 184 | 15884 | 67429 | 86612 | 47367 | 10242 | 44880 | 12060 | 44309 | 46629 | 55105 | 66793 | 93173 | 00480 | 13311 |
| 185 | 18745 | 32031 | 35303 | 08134 | 33925 | 03004 | 59929 | 95418 | 04917 | 57596 | 24878 | 61733 | 92834 | 64454 |
| 186 | 78934 | 40086 | 88292 | 65728 | 38300 | 42323 | 64068 | 98373 | 48971 | 09049 | 59943 | 36538 | 05976 | 82118 |
| 187 | 17626 | 02944 | 20910 | 57662 | 80181 | 38579 | 24580 | 90529 | 52303 | 50436 | 29401 | 57824 | 86039 | 81062 |
| 188 | 27117 | 61399 | 50967 | 41399 | 81636 | 16663 | 15634 | 79717 | 94696 | 59240 | 25543 | 97989 | 63306 | 90946 |
| 189 | 93995 | 18678 | 90012 | 63645 | 85701 | 85269 | 62263 | 68331 | 00389 | 72571 | 15210 | 20769 | 44686 | 96176 |
| 190 | 67392 | 89421 | 09623 | 80725 | 62620 | 84162 | 87368 | 29560 | 00519 | 84545 | 08004 | 24526 | 41252 | 14521 |
| 191 | 04910 | 12261 | 37566 | 80016 | 21245 | 69377 | 50420 | 85658 | 55263 | 68667 | 78770 | 04533 | 14513 | 18099 |
| 192 | 81453 | 20283 | 79929 | 59839 | 23875 | 13245 | 46808 | 74124 | 74703 | 35769 | 95588 | 21014 | 37078 | 39170 |
| 193 | 19480 | 75790 | 48539 | 23703 | 15537 | 48885 | 02861 | 86587 | 74539 | 65227 | 90799 | 58789 | 96257 | 02708 |
| 194 | 21456 | 13162 | 74608 | 81011 | 55512 | 07481 | 93551 | 72189 | 76261 | 91206 | 89941 | 15132 | 37738 | 59284 |
| 195 | 89406 | 20912 | 46189 | 76376 | 25538 | 87212 | 20748 | 12831 | 57166 | 35026 | 16817 | 79121 | 18929 | 40628 |
| 196 | 09866 | 07414 | 55977 | 16419 | 01101 | 69343 | 13305 | 94302 | 80703 | 57910 | 36933 | 57771 | 42546 | 03003 |
| 197 | 86541 | 24681 | 23421 | 13521 | 28000 | 94917 | 07423 | 57523 | 97234 | 63951 | 42876 | 46829 | 09781 | 58160 |
| 198 | 10414 | 96941 | 06205 | 72222 | 57167 | 83902 | 07460 | 69507 | 10600 | 08858 | 07685 | 44472 | 64220 | 27040 |
| 199 | 49942 | 06683 | 41479 | 58982 | 56288 | 42853 | 92196 | 20632 | 62045 | 78812 | 35895 | 51851 | 83534 | 10689 |
| 200 | 23995 | 68882 | 42291 | 23374 | 24299 | 27024 | 67460 | 94783 | 40937 | 16961 | 26053 | 78749 | 46704 | 21983 |

## TABLE 1

| Line \ Col. | (1) | (2) | (3) | (4) | (5) | (6) | (7) | (8) | (9) | (10) | (11) | (12) | (13) | (14) |
|---|---|---|---|---|---|---|---|---|---|---|---|---|---|---|
| 201 | 78994 | 36244 | 02673 | 25475 | 84953 | 61793 | 50243 | 63423 | 69309 | 80308 | 49977 | 18075 | 43227 | 08266 |
| 202 | 04909 | 58485 | 70686 | 93930 | 34880 | 73059 | 06823 | 80257 | 44193 | 08337 | 47655 | 75932 | 29209 | 41954 |
| 203 | 46582 | 73570 | 33004 | 51795 | 86477 | 46736 | 60460 | 70345 | 37322 | 19987 | 67143 | 41129 | 89514 | 46892 |
| 204 | 29242 | 89792 | 88634 | 60285 | 07190 | 07795 | 27011 | 85941 | 01852 | 43096 | 31173 | 43730 | 48505 | 17958 |
| 205 | 68104 | 81339 | 97090 | 20601 | 78940 | 20228 | 22803 | 96070 | 10251 | 62711 | 66200 | 74330 | 13820 | 18966 |
| 206 | 17156 | 02182 | 82504 | 19880 | 93747 | 80910 | 78260 | 25136 | 62018 | 62919 | 73801 | 57195 | 83457 | 70597 |
| 207 | 50711 | 94789 | 07171 | 02103 | 99057 | 98775 | 37997 | 18325 | 88281 | 61091 | 97889 | 79977 | 04544 | 72963 |
| 208 | 39449 | 52409 | 75095 | 77720 | 39729 | 03205 | 09313 | 43545 | 43786 | 70443 | 41350 | 73369 | 42405 | 80516 |
| 209 | 75629 | 82729 | 76916 | 72657 | 58992 | 32756 | 01154 | 84890 | 04107 | 17469 | 69346 | 68651 | 97433 | 89491 |
| 210 | 01020 | 55151 | 36132 | 51971 | 32155 | 60735 | 64867 | 35424 | 25257 | 93844 | 39928 | 52519 | 34368 | 02114 |
| 211 | 08337 | 89989 | 24260 | 08618 | 66798 | 25889 | 52860 | 57375 | 52815 | 43539 | 18072 | 44270 | 27309 | 56535 |
| 212 | 76829 | 47229 | 19706 | 30094 | 69430 | 92399 | 98749 | 22081 | 52564 | 90431 | 35208 | 40323 | 87505 | 10227 |
| 213 | 39708 | 30641 | 21267 | 56501 | 95182 | 72442 | 21445 | 17276 | 90344 | 33199 | 02522 | 97883 | 09515 | 65930 |
| 214 | 89836 | 55817 | 56747 | 75195 | 06818 | 83043 | 47403 | 58266 | 52630 | 75573 | 91088 | 41118 | 27195 | 40650 |
| 215 | 25903 | 61370 | 66081 | 54076 | 67442 | 52964 | 23823 | 02718 | 28786 | 06121 | 29680 | 55295 | 67086 | 57574 |
| 216 | 71345 | 03422 | 01015 | 68025 | 19703 | 77313 | 04555 | 83425 | 46763 | 95315 | 23150 | 15116 | 18017 | 42730 |
| 217 | 61454 | 92263 | 14647 | 08473 | 34124 | 10740 | 40839 | 05620 | 62418 | 73374 | 92577 | 06755 | 21856 | 56272 |
| 218 | 80376 | 08909 | 30470 | 40200 | 46558 | 61742 | 11643 | 92121 | 22294 | 26648 | 69676 | 46198 | 00331 | 85186 |
| 219 | 45144 | 54373 | 05505 | 90074 | 24783 | 86299 | 20900 | 15144 | 26506 | 53770 | 76431 | 23861 | 71208 | 80694 |
| 220 | 12191 | 88527 | 58852 | 51175 | 11534 | 87218 | 04876 | 85584 | 78465 | 82182 | 03412 | 13217 | 14313 | 70593 |
| 221 | 62936 | 59120 | 73957 | 35969 | 21598 | 47287 | 39394 | 08778 | 38036 | 30140 | 89117 | 32054 | 44603 | 61849 |
| 222 | 31588 | 96798 | 43668 | 12611 | 01714 | 77266 | 55079 | 24690 | 84716 | 77732 | 35363 | 85525 | 17015 | 56344 |
| 223 | 20787 | 96048 | 84726 | 17512 | 39450 | 43618 | 30629 | 24356 | 05294 | 34236 | 65299 | 36922 | 46995 | 65765 |
| 224 | 45603 | 00745 | 84635 | 43079 | 52724 | 14262 | 05750 | 89373 | 79088 | 38088 | 65082 | 92504 | 80545 | 03090 |
| 225 | 31606 | 64782 | 34027 | 56734 | 09365 | 20008 | 93559 | 78384 | 99219 | 61747 | 96111 | 86965 | 33233 | 29812 |
| 226 | 10452 | 33074 | 76718 | 99556 | 16026 | 00013 | 78411 | 95107 | 10786 | 44886 | 44612 | 06830 | 27848 | 87597 |
| 227 | 37016 | 64633 | 67301 | 50949 | 91298 | 74968 | 73631 | 57397 | 08632 | 04762 | 69328 | 34926 | 07403 | 60916 |
| 228 | 66725 | 97865 | 25409 | 37498 | 00816 | 99268 | 14471 | 10232 | 19035 | 21695 | 07540 | 96447 | 20743 | 92472 |
| 229 | 07380 | 74438 | 82120 | 17890 | 40963 | 55757 | 13492 | 68294 | 87170 | 49468 | 40164 | 13374 | 23021 | 17006 |
| 230 | 71621 | 57688 | 58256 | 47702 | 74724 | 89419 | 08025 | 68519 | 95138 | 54788 | 32999 | 34374 | 05780 | 17506 |
| 231 | 03466 | 13263 | 23917 | 20417 | 11315 | 52805 | 33072 | 07723 | 87876 | 75258 | 22709 | 99869 | 11609 | 46666 |
| 232 | 12692 | 32931 | 97387 | 34822 | 53775 | 91674 | 76549 | 37635 | 91118 | 31062 | 89441 | 31839 | 88614 | 78168 |
| 233 | 52192 | 30941 | 44998 | 17833 | 94563 | 23062 | 95725 | 38463 | 03665 | 49189 | 46359 | 37401 | 73407 | 61817 |
| 234 | 56691 | 72529 | 66063 | 73570 | 86660 | 68125 | 40436 | 31303 | 79330 | 59083 | 34862 | 00540 | 21734 | 75535 |
| 235 | 74952 | 43041 | 58869 | 15677 | 78598 | 43520 | 97521 | 83248 | 52173 | 17636 | 77106 | 01044 | 22990 | 74874 |
| 236 | 18752 | 43693 | 32867 | 53017 | 22661 | 39610 | 03796 | 02622 | 78267 | 24503 | 73518 | 76545 | 99088 | 08369 |
| 237 | 61691 | 04944 | 43111 | 28325 | 82319 | 65589 | 66048 | 98498 | 46941 | 81427 | 44447 | 70357 | 18864 | 15525 |
| 238 | 49197 | 63948 | 38947 | 60207 | 70667 | 39843 | 60607 | 15328 | 09528 | 17277 | 84278 | 04463 | 12188 | 35359 |
| 239 | 19436 | 87291 | 71684 | 74859 | 76501 | 93456 | 95714 | 92518 | 10683 | 75617 | 78841 | 25315 | 74041 | 71554 |
| 240 | 39143 | 64893 | 14606 | 13543 | 09621 | 68301 | 69817 | 52140 | 03976 | 48795 | 60266 | 99592 | 68334 | 18790 |
| 241 | 82244 | 67549 | 76491 | 09761 | 74494 | 91307 | 64222 | 66592 | 67270 | 38593 | 18094 | 95095 | 08649 | 25047 |
| 242 | 55847 | 56155 | 42878 | 23708 | 97999 | 40131 | 52360 | 90390 | 73108 | 40475 | 80487 | 07787 | 35238 | 50990 |
| 243 | 94095 | 95970 | 07826 | 25991 | 37584 | 56966 | 68623 | 83454 | 49461 | 97707 | 12479 | 25041 | 40565 | 18313 |
| 244 | 11751 | 69469 | 25521 | 44097 | 07511 | 88976 | 30122 | 67542 | 54825 | 03274 | 02765 | 67162 | 40312 | 76127 |
| 245 | 69902 | 08995 | 27821 | 11758 | 64989 | 61902 | 32121 | 28165 | 21326 | 97375 | 44801 | 66977 | 08232 | 06807 |
| 246 | 21850 | 25352 | 25556 | 92161 | 23592 | 43294 | 10479 | 37879 | 21825 | 11453 | 29584 | 70067 | 09471 | 16319 |
| 247 | 75850 | 46992 | 25165 | 55906 | 62339 | 88958 | 91717 | 15756 | 78817 | 35541 | 01177 | 06869 | 10543 | 57652 |
| 248 | 29648 | 22086 | 42581 | 85677 | 20251 | 39641 | 65786 | 80689 | 49066 | 14456 | 91681 | 69371 | 18292 | 39377 |
| 249 | 82740 | 28443 | 42734 | 25518 | 82827 | 35825 | 90288 | 32911 | 79666 | 52959 | 01475 | 83321 | 24991 | 80102 |
| 250 | 36842 | 42092 | 52075 | 83926 | 42875 | 71500 | 69216 | 01350 | 92846 | 84792 | 87455 | 06842 | 22422 | 77379 |

TABLE 1

| Line \ Col. | (1) | (2) | (3) | (4) | (5) | (6) | (7) | (8) | (9) | (10) | (11) | (12) | (13) | (14) |
|---|---|---|---|---|---|---|---|---|---|---|---|---|---|---|
| 251 | 89429 | 26726 | 15563 | 94972 | 78739 | 04419 | 60523 | 31022 | 23728 | 37647 | 16476 | 11170 | 68376 | 56874 |
| 252 | 43427 | 25412 | 25587 | 21276 | 44426 | 17369 | 29010 | 45337 | 90845 | 98053 | 41447 | 14897 | 18753 | 68291 |
| 253 | 58575 | 81958 | 51846 | 02676 | 67781 | 95137 | 88430 | 78260 | 66962 | 31812 | 12759 | 06427 | 40337 | 50115 |
| 254 | 61888 | 71246 | 24246 | 23487 | 78639 | 92006 | 63846 | 92263 | 33212 | 26516 | 93662 | 72399 | 88244 | 33922 |
| 255 | 73891 | 47025 | 40937 | 71907 | 26827 | 98865 | 38882 | 25757 | 26662 | 91441 | 89357 | 87803 | 61521 | 80600 |
| 256 | 40938 | 73894 | 40854 | 15997 | 55293 | 95033 | 31736 | 75068 | 91314 | 75293 | 04895 | 39355 | 54837 | 57203 |
| 257 | 98053 | 43567 | 17292 | 86908 | 71364 | 06089 | 92394 | 73691 | 57883 | 09983 | 35643 | 79309 | 53449 | 95334 |
| 258 | 59774 | 29138 | 46993 | 39836 | 99596 | 59050 | 25419 | 04130 | 54632 | 17223 | 94604 | 22973 | 97731 | 99476 |
| 259 | 09765 | 07548 | 63043 | 59782 | 81449 | 13652 | 94420 | 74460 | 46707 | 94303 | 85523 | 95844 | 70995 | 10742 |
| 260 | 38991 | 64502 | 24770 | 29209 | 82909 | 66610 | 84418 | 66214 | 26001 | 78685 | 69117 | 72446 | 79783 | 22305 |
| 261 | 25622 | 27100 | 56128 | 62145 | 82388 | 45197 | 97609 | 83942 | 01120 | 71717 | 32858 | 58679 | 97165 | 02810 |
| 262 | 31864 | 74120 | 66231 | 82306 | 91784 | 33177 | 17681 | 18963 | 07216 | 49288 | 43185 | 62797 | 00735 | 27085 |
| 263 | 81171 | 75639 | 60863 | 49562 | 28846 | 81581 | 10249 | 23190 | 53440 | 32357 | 16472 | 99013 | 24328 | 93670 |
| 264 | 69874 | 52803 | 28544 | 51569 | 56090 | 44558 | 42095 | 92311 | 57915 | 13368 | 13719 | 15833 | 38744 | 56065 |
| 265 | 27848 | 51107 | 05761 | 02159 | 53911 | 01952 | 59273 | 32250 | 39647 | 29908 | 49075 | 23061 | 07795 | 95047 |
| 266 | 69407 | 69736 | 75375 | 31488 | 67528 | 84234 | 76462 | 13628 | 21286 | 13736 | 67478 | 45218 | 27867 | 93049 |
| 267 | 29418 | 03091 | 06364 | 13151 | 40663 | 43633 | 87954 | 69800 | 24773 | 62596 | 52476 | 60631 | 50503 | 94116 |
| 268 | 38222 | 31231 | 79415 | 44558 | 62490 | 26936 | 49682 | 16307 | 98535 | 44822 | 99574 | 58487 | 85020 | 68881 |
| 269 | 94720 | 83796 | 93251 | 03568 | 62484 | 29140 | 14152 | 37044 | 90398 | 92042 | 35099 | 31640 | 99753 | 44409 |
| 270 | 45275 | 16852 | 02284 | 41361 | 73733 | 61486 | 33189 | 08907 | 41159 | 08147 | 15478 | 33250 | 17361 | 79961 |
| 271 | 97260 | 09552 | 82626 | 42915 | 45847 | 87401 | 13339 | 53850 | 34931 | 00602 | 75307 | 99708 | 77863 | 04924 |
| 272 | 01990 | 65259 | 60684 | 78175 | 43825 | 45211 | 86287 | 78190 | 02431 | 66251 | 74970 | 50246 | 23975 | 80697 |
| 273 | 24633 | 42314 | 81192 | 50253 | 67516 | 59076 | 92006 | 65676 | 87343 | 89231 | 15760 | 73706 | 69426 | 01979 |
| 274 | 98071 | 52677 | 74920 | 74461 | 52266 | 26967 | 68284 | 31612 | 40335 | 28865 | 98949 | 64492 | 96905 | 29184 |
| 275 | 34101 | 79442 | 88403 | 48541 | 13010 | 16596 | 72001 | 38546 | 76305 | 22119 | 82668 | 84017 | 44111 | 40302 |
| 276 | 77186 | 93967 | 25918 | 66403 | 73837 | 73445 | 86663 | 15929 | 08237 | 05647 | 15785 | 70444 | 58670 | 95967 |
| 277 | 23114 | 05481 | 42335 | 51396 | 60823 | 22680 | 50459 | 05429 | 35227 | 92559 | 24136 | 13126 | 22099 | 52388 |
| 278 | 59988 | 49944 | 41038 | 99977 | 16348 | 41119 | 51548 | 19511 | 90142 | 65604 | 16147 | 63445 | 60525 | 10480 |
| 279 | 11852 | 42254 | 82304 | 05588 | 75165 | 20179 | 94198 | 25700 | 33473 | 59554 | 30974 | 69973 | 57629 | 38550 |
| 280 | 59992 | 87922 | 56299 | 01700 | 07003 | 97507 | 69260 | 53349 | 86947 | 27517 | 80159 | 01899 | 46890 | 53850 |
| 281 | 42116 | 86593 | 22828 | 41422 | 18176 | 03250 | 06079 | 85467 | 32052 | 56922 | 96804 | 51060 | 33157 | 83948 |
| 282 | 39663 | 61401 | 21471 | 42702 | 70588 | 53144 | 27087 | 05591 | 57759 | 51394 | 98873 | 45625 | 61069 | 78783 |
| 283 | 53542 | 72009 | 96296 | 68908 | 58657 | 87117 | 21483 | 28879 | 20480 | 57309 | 95552 | 09826 | 79928 | 17141 |
| 284 | 25996 | 76108 | 98476 | 36397 | 89457 | 19577 | 65877 | 04802 | 61938 | 25032 | 09190 | 74932 | 36925 | 82686 |
| 285 | 91106 | 26450 | 14451 | 50328 | 29084 | 32332 | 08635 | 25192 | 31337 | 20249 | 95073 | 93800 | 70022 | 99968 |
| 286 | 37133 | 88924 | 27845 | 13024 | 90687 | 23726 | 11212 | 30414 | 42185 | 49224 | 46560 | 80447 | 24334 | 74866 |
| 287 | 13982 | 25736 | 10087 | 16762 | 02564 | 27250 | 79316 | 83848 | 38684 | 20552 | 44402 | 85153 | 94526 | 41256 |
| 288 | 26663 | 36187 | 81688 | 25005 | 46677 | 75851 | 73938 | 73044 | 05132 | 61204 | 90384 | 90296 | 03182 | 36672 |
| 289 | 62572 | 08275 | 16313 | 24936 | 61690 | 53829 | 40412 | 01479 | 24241 | 58488 | 65341 | 93414 | 07135 | 43446 |
| 290 | 65925 | 95455 | 08383 | 24643 | 72962 | 08172 | 37824 | 87587 | 40698 | 34964 | 50166 | 74756 | 77033 | 41501 |
| 291 | 97978 | 74676 | 08942 | 48919 | 51592 | 71196 | 48534 | 16955 | 25759 | 95645 | 03148 | 10646 | 15660 | 86520 |
| 292 | 01914 | 42524 | 67820 | 47985 | 91773 | 10383 | 89514 | 07557 | 02084 | 16736 | 39198 | 69697 | 62485 | 61938 |
| 293 | 68565 | 44811 | 39238 | 70394 | 78555 | 33539 | 56310 | 40809 | 63204 | 14479 | 19635 | 97299 | 66947 | 58010 |
| 294 | 54370 | 31672 | 03893 | 32423 | 54092 | 69375 | 63308 | 00016 | 28407 | 98287 | 22874 | 57545 | 72695 | 01604 |
| 295 | 79954 | 89601 | 23881 | 46951 | 69084 | 33477 | 87968 | 15639 | 82409 | 34185 | 36864 | 52112 | 27102 | 87334 |
| 296 | 55479 | 01059 | 44229 | 56975 | 05785 | 80930 | 26443 | 44898 | 77561 | 51123 | 34495 | 31376 | 06238 | 15973 |
| 297 | 38114 | 70330 | 42157 | 86699 | 46212 | 74692 | 92603 | 91306 | 58558 | 57280 | 50639 | 20563 | 71370 | 81487 |
| 298 | 29766 | 83452 | 66202 | 02488 | 72704 | 97821 | 70614 | 53616 | 39050 | 30355 | 15340 | 97298 | 41795 | 35185 |
| 299 | 31771 | 70640 | 34779 | 41831 | 33456 | 53194 | 19602 | 74194 | 61154 | 51774 | 76822 | 73794 | 54182 | 45264 |
| 300 | 77522 | 87188 | 83577 | 99067 | 83235 | 48662 | 31503 | 54829 | 54723 | 13177 | 15387 | 26073 | 68915 | 88415 |

## TABLE 1

| Line \ Col. | (1) | (2) | (3) | (4) | (5) | (6) | (7) | (8) | (9) | (10) | (11) | (12) | (13) | (14) |
|---|---|---|---|---|---|---|---|---|---|---|---|---|---|---|
| 301 | 64670 | 10396 | 82981 | 58320 | 71478 | 08143 | 48294 | 42631 | 45464 | 58092 | 14187 | 12271 | 98179 | 87812 |
| 302 | 25771 | 02205 | 73984 | 28436 | 88192 | 11470 | 11775 | 67385 | 66360 | 59884 | 93873 | 29948 | 66302 | 82227 |
| 303 | 27551 | 13537 | 54984 | 89406 | 88326 | 33993 | 92324 | 13249 | 35271 | 60400 | 70762 | 08343 | 76456 | 90068 |
| 304 | 91224 | 22417 | 44820 | 26189 | 57541 | 87558 | 45835 | 28461 | 54835 | 92411 | 44369 | 47512 | 49508 | 02841 |
| 305 | 75179 | 64320 | 71523 | 67868 | 38883 | 09674 | 27645 | 76240 | 47587 | 01677 | 38342 | 85598 | 12482 | 30749 |
| 306 | 64654 | 91085 | 65818 | 03313 | 39273 | 46384 | 66677 | 14148 | 87552 | 38383 | 67435 | 21072 | 63866 | 74644 |
| 307 | 98059 | 81123 | 67832 | 04102 | 66188 | 78200 | 67466 | 46043 | 65406 | 22834 | 08620 | 17509 | 51424 | 25187 |
| 308 | 38765 | 63585 | 18810 | 95805 | 11414 | 58096 | 00295 | 82626 | 42683 | 44518 | 12209 | 83245 | 53771 | 95469 |
| 309 | 01921 | 03564 | 71754 | 10213 | 80383 | 13473 | 94128 | 62199 | 59411 | 46782 | 62871 | 51149 | 87146 | 40129 |
| 310 | 16211 | 93671 | 27704 | 66778 | 96307 | 06732 | 63750 | 04191 | 40003 | 51653 | 54228 | 14916 | 05361 | 08884 |
| 311 | 70832 | 86076 | 61527 | 56123 | 48514 | 53935 | 86784 | 42351 | 67586 | 07432 | 61499 | 01773 | 97463 | 58815 |
| 312 | 22332 | 94265 | 67627 | 85815 | 00394 | 75271 | 98385 | 53697 | 56378 | 50592 | 77441 | 88505 | 89791 | 16331 |
| 313 | 81333 | 45965 | 64171 | 84367 | 15052 | 37965 | 03122 | 81914 | 69381 | 70034 | 92563 | 61804 | 58326 | 97895 |
| 314 | 39333 | 47453 | 66174 | 04546 | 10594 | 64271 | 61026 | 39471 | 55981 | 18628 | 67943 | 35599 | 37209 | 34061 |
| 315 | 29195 | 20825 | 50878 | 80273 | 26285 | 90070 | 79586 | 12449 | 77293 | 36577 | 59192 | 03658 | 90056 | 83145 |
| 316 | 74420 | 64037 | 06960 | 25109 | 08821 | 60143 | 34485 | 19257 | 29417 | 72713 | 72326 | 41572 | 41553 | 46946 |
| 317 | 22763 | 16508 | 24866 | 13177 | 07464 | 51730 | 65802 | 95718 | 28560 | 11332 | 74272 | 59189 | 53167 | 13133 |
| 318 | 72919 | 54618 | 40616 | 33287 | 51274 | 78491 | 53604 | 66742 | 97777 | 64468 | 98224 | 45485 | 17257 | 31561 |
| 319 | 92385 | 42402 | 15922 | 90033 | 21555 | 31647 | 22288 | 75692 | 20592 | 84620 | 58679 | 24587 | 83517 | 55327 |
| 320 | 85431 | 19857 | 97246 | 46118 | 71222 | 82744 | 67892 | 77155 | 10785 | 00344 | 19641 | 98279 | 18716 | 13895 |
| 321 | 40778 | 12451 | 14921 | 51464 | 45331 | 75822 | 46859 | 66829 | 35803 | 27645 | 76095 | 41535 | 25508 | 53066 |
| 322 | 88903 | 46592 | 60637 | 65231 | 08778 | 86813 | 47819 | 19218 | 46837 | 89671 | 77661 | 08518 | 85216 | 62664 |
| 323 | 29830 | 34899 | 85457 | 19548 | 83355 | 52479 | 77801 | 01596 | 48890 | 56104 | 68733 | 40830 | 58611 | 59181 |
| 324 | 22832 | 47422 | 08073 | 10107 | 46772 | 92299 | 42975 | 86376 | 27869 | 52954 | 07900 | 75918 | 51398 | 87598 |
| 325 | 75159 | 14809 | 11930 | 83531 | 51239 | 86298 | 72661 | 63015 | 98804 | 98491 | 99565 | 42801 | 71816 | 84000 |
| 326 | 99390 | 08217 | 56276 | 09263 | 82685 | 30451 | 25742 | 41105 | 74711 | 42007 | 02082 | 93025 | 86641 | 28952 |
| 327 | 68622 | 80897 | 08902 | 10867 | 91379 | 30068 | 84289 | 45020 | 92459 | 03831 | 08531 | 63496 | 98230 | 42884 |
| 328 | 92393 | 95901 | 41179 | 72129 | 72502 | 91097 | 09488 | 84896 | 37720 | 68104 | 73817 | 67626 | 16221 | 63527 |
| 329 | 53122 | 66033 | 38229 | 51879 | 29925 | 45574 | 53938 | 72801 | 64067 | 76328 | 28941 | 43645 | 37181 | 95329 |
| 330 | 43251 | 11941 | 86631 | 93264 | 53433 | 70281 | 55000 | 24550 | 74751 | 32855 | 25399 | 95743 | 85393 | 20261 |
| 331 | 16613 | 24901 | 34866 | 75002 | 55163 | 68308 | 20070 | 36953 | 39378 | 71191 | 84510 | 47599 | 93608 | 24379 |
| 332 | 12010 | 60852 | 92603 | 70393 | 17989 | 95755 | 14672 | 58786 | 41996 | 02893 | 94163 | 36156 | 54203 | 94138 |
| 333 | 85528 | 97879 | 27814 | 08219 | 02908 | 71582 | 31439 | 00360 | 72264 | 87245 | 65903 | 42298 | 28061 | 81889 |
| 334 | 32590 | 55079 | 33556 | 83169 | 92087 | 77939 | 53792 | 78795 | 58159 | 86394 | 41749 | 91623 | 26973 | 81474 |
| 335 | 92934 | 30650 | 16449 | 15805 | 61551 | 38689 | 59179 | 85485 | 18537 | 70496 | 98694 | 19796 | 76804 | 03673 |
| 336 | 80614 | 10150 | 09389 | 61892 | 79477 | 14522 | 40270 | 45744 | 29588 | 29717 | 39590 | 10223 | 43049 | 78775 |
| 337 | 62398 | 12034 | 90764 | 52872 | 22285 | 50592 | 42505 | 80560 | 38213 | 18917 | 10015 | 03887 | 62589 | 15851 |
| 338 | 02222 | 46811 | 05145 | 67916 | 15184 | 02636 | 59078 | 57773 | 21259 | 86090 | 56705 | 65566 | 04487 | 95954 |
| 339 | 08690 | 31785 | 61664 | 61322 | 24149 | 21471 | 23328 | 03093 | 31266 | 14840 | 30703 | 01640 | 07874 | 16630 |
| 340 | 61187 | 73897 | 66168 | 12885 | 73191 | 89432 | 65414 | 41886 | 75911 | 35708 | 43208 | 59193 | 04727 | 31037 |
| 341 | 12324 | 61149 | 85643 | 64999 | 63738 | 46671 | 25408 | 69313 | 54455 | 04917 | 35047 | 09951 | 72776 | 84697 |
| 342 | 47635 | 42279 | 98620 | 70677 | 52386 | 50904 | 97403 | 03931 | 42090 | 28179 | 98028 | 47728 | 45696 | 74176 |
| 343 | 70965 | 00390 | 08878 | 15373 | 70276 | 71889 | 86953 | 37931 | 23286 | 20508 | 40100 | 22486 | 37323 | 35429 |
| 344 | 58764 | 15262 | 96814 | 54548 | 00042 | 19721 | 78869 | 85937 | 36639 | 29135 | 12633 | 67225 | 69588 | 74178 |
| 345 | 07429 | 05609 | 31207 | 50254 | 68389 | 07714 | 92268 | 64698 | 32823 | 60122 | 46213 | 05646 | 54742 | 98304 |
| 346 | 15665 | 28659 | 54952 | 53217 | 76898 | 88931 | 25786 | 55912 | 85269 | 29212 | 84976 | 08888 | 94332 | 58528 |
| 347 | 64208 | 53232 | 99459 | 43605 | 04553 | 48451 | 68154 | 49436 | 49891 | 65524 | 65133 | 55163 | 76765 | 26006 |
| 348 | 17952 | 73276 | 52567 | 48489 | 64264 | 24220 | 55498 | 97548 | 98437 | 26033 | 39026 | 17377 | 43519 | 27425 |
| 349 | 60531 | 43217 | 39999 | 38615 | 97195 | 76928 | 87688 | 99010 | 90189 | 12522 | 00675 | 01995 | 82781 | 95130 |
| 350 | 76692 | 39999 | 43254 | 68110 | 88053 | 88727 | 14187 | 98623 | 84225 | 78440 | 67082 | 37425 | 40559 | 16838 |

| Line \ Col. | (1) | (2) | (3) | (4) | (5) | (6) | (7) | (8) | (9) | (10) | (11) | (12) | (13) | (14) |
|---|---|---|---|---|---|---|---|---|---|---|---|---|---|---|
| 351 | 06433 | 80674 | 24520 | 18222 | 10610 | 05794 | 37515 | 48619 | 62866 | 33963 | 14045 | 79451 | 04934 | 45576 |
| 352 | 39298 | 47829 | 72648 | 37414 | 75755 | 04717 | 29899 | 78817 | 03509 | 78673 | 73181 | 29973 | 18664 | 04555 |
| 353 | 89884 | 59651 | 67533 | 68123 | 17730 | 95862 | 08034 | 19473 | 63971 | 37271 | 31445 | 49019 | 49405 | 46925 |
| 354 | 61512 | 32155 | 51906 | 61662 | 64130 | 16688 | 37275 | 51262 | 11569 | 08697 | 91120 | 64156 | 40365 | 74297 |
| 355 | 99653 | 47635 | 12506 | 88535 | 36553 | 23757 | 34209 | 55803 | 96275 | 26130 | 47949 | 14877 | 69594 | 83041 |
| 356 | 95913 | 11085 | 13772 | 76638 | 48423 | 25018 | 99041 | 77529 | 81360 | 18180 | 97421 | 55541 | 90275 | 18213 |
| 357 | 55864 | 44004 | 13122 | 44115 | 01601 | 50541 | 00147 | 77685 | 58788 | 33016 | 61173 | 93049 | 04694 | 43534 |
| 358 | 35334 | 82410 | 91601 | 40617 | 72876 | 33967 | 73830 | 15405 | 96554 | 88265 | 34537 | 38526 | 67924 | 40474 |
| 359 | 57729 | 88646 | 76487 | 11622 | 96297 | 24160 | 09903 | 14047 | 22917 | 60718 | 66487 | 46346 | 30949 | 03173 |
| 360 | 86648 | 89317 | 63677 | 70119 | 94739 | 25875 | 38829 | 68377 | 43918 | 77653 | 04127 | 69930 | 43283 | 35766 |
| 361 | 30574 | 06039 | 07967 | 32422 | 76791 | 39725 | 53711 | 93385 | 13421 | 67957 | 20384 | 58731 | 53396 | 59723 |
| 362 | 81307 | 13114 | 83580 | 79974 | 45929 | 85113 | 72268 | 09858 | 52104 | 32014 | 53115 | 03727 | 98624 | 84616 |
| 363 | 02410 | 96385 | 79007 | 54939 | 21410 | 86980 | 91772 | 93307 | 34116 | 49516 | 42148 | 57740 | 31198 | 70336 |
| 364 | 18969 | 87444 | 52233 | 62319 | 08598 | 09066 | 95288 | 04794 | 01534 | 92058 | 03157 | 91758 | 80611 | 45357 |
| 365 | 87863 | 80514 | 66860 | 62297 | 80198 | 19347 | 73234 | 86265 | 49096 | 97021 | 92882 | 61422 | 75890 | 86442 |
| 366 | 68397 | 10538 | 15438 | 62311 | 72844 | 60203 | 46412 | 65943 | 79232 | 45702 | 67055 | 39024 | 57383 | 44424 |
| 367 | 28529 | 45247 | 58729 | 10854 | 99058 | 18260 | 38765 | 90038 | 94209 | 04055 | 27393 | 61517 | 23002 | 96560 |
| 368 | 44285 | 09452 | 15867 | 70418 | 57012 | 72122 | 36634 | 97283 | 95943 | 78363 | 36498 | 40662 | 94188 | 18202 |
| 369 | 86299 | 22510 | 33571 | 23309 | 57040 | 29285 | 67870 | 21913 | 72958 | 75637 | 99936 | 58715 | 07943 | 23748 |
| 370 | 84842 | 05748 | 90894 | 61658 | 15001 | 94055 | 36308 | 41161 | 37341 | 81838 | 19389 | 80336 | 46346 | 91895 |
| 371 | 56970 | 10799 | 52098 | 04184 | 54967 | 72938 | 56834 | 23777 | 98392 | 31417 | 98547 | 92058 | 02277 | 50315 |
| 372 | 83125 | 85077 | 60490 | 44369 | 66130 | 72936 | 69848 | 59973 | 08144 | 61070 | 73094 | 27059 | 69181 | 55623 |
| 373 | 55503 | 21383 | 02464 | 26141 | 68779 | 66388 | 75242 | 82690 | 74099 | 77885 | 23813 | 10054 | 11900 | 44653 |
| 374 | 47019 | 06683 | 33203 | 29608 | 54553 | 25971 | 69573 | 83854 | 24715 | 48866 | 65745 | 31131 | 47636 | 45137 |
| 375 | 84828 | 61152 | 79526 | 29554 | 84580 | 37859 | 28504 | 61980 | 34997 | 41825 | 11623 | 07320 | 15003 | 56774 |
| 376 | 68921 | 31331 | 79827 | 05748 | 51876 | 57143 | 31926 | 99915 | 45821 | 97702 | 87125 | 44488 | 77613 | 56823 |
| 377 | 36458 | 28285 | 30424 | 98420 | 72925 | 40729 | 22337 | 48293 | 86847 | 43186 | 42951 | 37804 | 85129 | 28993 |
| 378 | 95752 | 96065 | 36847 | 87729 | 81679 | 59126 | 59437 | 33225 | 31280 | 41232 | 34750 | 91097 | 60752 | 69783 |
| 379 | 26768 | 02513 | 58454 | 56958 | 20575 | 76746 | 49878 | 06846 | 32828 | 24425 | 30249 | 78801 | 26977 | 92074 |
| 380 | 42613 | 72456 | 43636 | 58085 | 06766 | 60227 | 96414 | 32671 | 45587 | 79620 | 84831 | 38156 | 74211 | 82752 |
| 381 | 95457 | 12176 | 65482 | 25596 | 02678 | 54592 | 63607 | 82096 | 21913 | 75544 | 55228 | 89796 | 05694 | 91552 |
| 382 | 95276 | 67524 | 63564 | 95958 | 39750 | 64379 | 46059 | 51666 | 10433 | 10945 | 55306 | 78562 | 89630 | 41230 |
| 383 | 66954 | 53574 | 64776 | 92345 | 95110 | 59448 | 77249 | 54044 | 67942 | 24145 | 42294 | 27427 | 84875 | 37022 |
| 384 | 17457 | 44151 | 14113 | 62462 | 02798 | 54977 | 48349 | 66738 | 60184 | 75679 | 38120 | 17640 | 36242 | 99357 |
| 385 | 03704 | 23322 | 83214 | 59337 | 01695 | 60666 | 97410 | 55064 | 17427 | 89180 | 74018 | 44865 | 53197 | 74810 |
| 386 | 21538 | 16997 | 33210 | 60337 | 27976 | 70661 | 08250 | 69599 | 60264 | 84549 | 78007 | 88450 | 06488 | 72274 |
| 387 | 57178 | 16739 | 98310 | 70348 | 11317 | 71623 | 55510 | 64756 | 87759 | 92354 | 78694 | 63638 | 80939 | 98644 |
| 388 | 31048 | 40058 | 94953 | 55866 | 96283 | 46620 | 52087 | 80817 | 74533 | 68407 | 55862 | 32476 | 19326 | 95558 |
| 389 | 69799 | 83300 | 16498 | 80733 | 96422 | 58078 | 99643 | 39847 | 96884 | 84657 | 33697 | 39578 | 90197 | 80532 |
| 390 | 90595 | 65017 | 59231 | 17772 | 67831 | 33317 | 00520 | 90401 | 41700 | 95510 | 61166 | 33757 | 23279 | 85523 |
| 391 | 33570 | 34761 | 98939 | 78784 | 09977 | 29398 | 93896 | 78227 | 90110 | 81378 | 96639 | 37008 | 04050 | 04228 |
| 392 | 15340 | 82760 | 57477 | 13898 | 48431 | 72936 | 78160 | 87240 | 52716 | 87697 | 79433 | 16336 | 52862 | 69149 |
| 393 | 64079 | 07733 | 36512 | 56186 | 99098 | 48850 | 72527 | 08486 | 10951 | 26832 | 39763 | 02485 | 71688 | 90936 |
| 394 | 63491 | 84886 | 67118 | 62063 | 74958 | 20946 | 28147 | 39338 | 32169 | 03713 | 93510 | 61244 | 73774 | 01245 |
| 395 | 92003 | 76568 | 41034 | 28260 | 79708 | 00770 | 88643 | 21188 | 01850 | 69689 | 49426 | 49128 | 14660 | 14143 |
| 396 | 52360 | 46658 | 66511 | 04172 | 73085 | 11795 | 52594 | 13287 | 82531 | 04388 | 64693 | 11934 | 35051 | 68576 |
| 397 | 74622 | 12142 | 68355 | 65635 | 21828 | 39539 | 18988 | 53609 | 04001 | 19648 | 14083 | 49623 | 10840 | 31915 |
| 398 | 04157 | 50079 | 61343 | 64315 | 70836 | 82857 | 35335 | 87900 | 36194 | 31567 | 53506 | 34304 | 39910 | 79630 |
| 399 | 86003 | 60070 | 66241 | 32836 | 27573 | 11479 | 94114 | 81641 | 00496 | 36058 | 75899 | 46620 | 70024 | 88753 |
| 400 | 41268 | 80187 | 20351 | 09636 | 84668 | 42486 | 71303 | 19512 | 50277 | 71508 | 20116 | 79520 | 06269 | 74173 |

TABLE 1

| Line \ Col. | (1) | (2) | (3) | (4) | (5) | (6) | (7) | (8) | (9) | (10) | (11) | (12) | (13) | (14) |
|---|---|---|---|---|---|---|---|---|---|---|---|---|---|---|
| 401 | 05073 | 90103 | 85167 | 53900 | 19720 | 41488 | 57476 | 39458 | 16621 | 69774 | 47953 | 35039 | 39283 | 21573 |
| 402 | 93320 | 80269 | 56684 | 39192 | 53220 | 74539 | 26393 | 00787 | 94490 | 23386 | 38454 | 33466 | 32159 | 77439 |
| 403 | 18806 | 70257 | 96424 | 13606 | 14356 | 76599 | 25390 | 63236 | 04513 | 16358 | 30540 | 10551 | 32498 | 18685 |
| 404 | 22253 | 45923 | 29815 | 18578 | 23316 | 30896 | 64771 | 11220 | 86218 | 75956 | 22399 | 36234 | 61644 | 80682 |
| 405 | 93640 | 45982 | 40011 | 74142 | 29106 | 45729 | 43406 | 21457 | 04301 | 39651 | 76025 | 73819 | 11462 | 97385 |
| 406 | 47630 | 45980 | 76619 | 57138 | 57492 | 00030 | 77897 | 76236 | 64990 | 35985 | 57748 | 11606 | 72081 | 18359 |
| 407 | 01781 | 55061 | 07455 | 47083 | 71870 | 90597 | 10151 | 59606 | 96919 | 31174 | 99872 | 15843 | 99173 | 79512 |
| 408 | 69694 | 45054 | 33587 | 03664 | 95007 | 31567 | 25334 | 26433 | 75002 | 67607 | 33135 | 07076 | 82984 | 82675 |
| 409 | 51236 | 05052 | 26503 | 94651 | 29874 | 73492 | 88941 | 08488 | 09418 | 08173 | 63380 | 82067 | 58143 | 64983 |
| 410 | 89445 | 51039 | 73837 | 26720 | 38650 | 47322 | 68474 | 95047 | 20404 | 41577 | 46865 | 39849 | 78735 | 99192 |
| 411 | 40867 | 96834 | 02162 | 41517 | 88937 | 26099 | 56047 | 49164 | 35127 | 64916 | 75451 | 79160 | 14014 | 00445 |
| 412 | 92946 | 56944 | 93407 | 05010 | 54896 | 33173 | 30548 | 23667 | 43171 | 47849 | 40449 | 91072 | 91092 | 17613 |
| 413 | 75898 | 02275 | 90768 | 31902 | 52114 | 36634 | 46803 | 97970 | 92216 | 55398 | 75320 | 70475 | 82931 | 20172 |
| 414 | 22729 | 21695 | 90824 | 80500 | 09332 | 54667 | 46696 | 38166 | 02005 | 24615 | 85613 | 25948 | 75389 | 25765 |
| 415 | 28733 | 62663 | 23644 | 16416 | 47135 | 39137 | 62190 | 31032 | 58702 | 03805 | 67252 | 23712 | 92697 | 19071 |
| 416 | 51323 | 37770 | 42114 | 79742 | 59905 | 38480 | 25293 | 32993 | 36946 | 62701 | 51198 | 72941 | 52215 | 85257 |
| 417 | 69325 | 65551 | 49927 | 68073 | 56979 | 49454 | 79451 | 60753 | 70872 | 07422 | 06399 | 75240 | 80847 | 78231 |
| 418 | 11333 | 60801 | 36992 | 76128 | 27959 | 41306 | 93543 | 15926 | 99159 | 27102 | 98684 | 80175 | 98732 | 45405 |
| 419 | 86347 | 03703 | 36778 | 72501 | 95229 | 65735 | 14269 | 50220 | 77270 | 68604 | 05677 | 23347 | 43686 | 31584 |
| 420 | 73452 | 36179 | 82893 | 92262 | 43850 | 31888 | 71151 | 40682 | 49775 | 63628 | 45415 | 96270 | 31735 | 01509 |
| 421 | 75483 | 74009 | 73699 | 05870 | 36804 | 89338 | 73891 | 40740 | 98753 | 74566 | 74733 | 34777 | 05786 | 38294 |
| 422 | 73302 | 84917 | 75128 | 34085 | 86208 | 98399 | 79433 | 61960 | 01720 | 87458 | 24023 | 89971 | 09532 | 68155 |
| 423 | 42785 | 24350 | 05933 | 65282 | 12832 | 75382 | 29826 | 33197 | 81781 | 53542 | 63985 | 57022 | 22712 | 61343 |
| 424 | 40429 | 33209 | 58622 | 09308 | 38098 | 55947 | 12001 | 73526 | 23170 | 13721 | 37856 | 86502 | 74299 | 01346 |
| 425 | 92876 | 58271 | 99325 | 12301 | 72957 | 22690 | 62705 | 73892 | 01974 | 77759 | 92733 | 11331 | 08323 | 86196 |
| 426 | 32951 | 39844 | 99126 | 94838 | 48715 | 36586 | 42076 | 15283 | 19280 | 29166 | 24522 | 73131 | 83401 | 38920 |
| 427 | 09772 | 28139 | 48130 | 73301 | 35915 | 90923 | 19255 | 75242 | 84655 | 30163 | 75510 | 83315 | 98529 | 93805 |
| 428 | 78459 | 91322 | 50072 | 77941 | 65046 | 78363 | 21951 | 42319 | 46472 | 67617 | 34134 | 05905 | 61251 | 51040 |
| 429 | 14419 | 96517 | 99075 | 43664 | 81119 | 63487 | 95589 | 51785 | 07398 | 23245 | 10086 | 49097 | 46173 | 00507 |
| 430 | 97769 | 50967 | 24427 | 21011 | 92226 | 44380 | 23422 | 10654 | 43617 | 80504 | 90663 | 60751 | 79728 | 41132 |
| 431 | 09175 | 37545 | 39088 | 06879 | 21277 | 05153 | 81855 | 84043 | 35307 | 59465 | 75395 | 74758 | 09427 | 84460 |
| 432 | 52062 | 95519 | 54087 | 14072 | 50953 | 63477 | 64635 | 34552 | 75243 | 70222 | 75023 | 81454 | 70606 | 31861 |
| 433 | 70558 | 85169 | 01086 | 97202 | 10390 | 01819 | 88167 | 21851 | 87837 | 85287 | 69883 | 08289 | 74968 | 46947 |
| 434 | 22553 | 61317 | 08968 | 67521 | 16627 | 48855 | 97263 | 94242 | 93354 | 72446 | 28840 | 88195 | 82751 | 94352 |
| 435 | 95216 | 75263 | 60351 | 02643 | 00063 | 20824 | 67468 | 89441 | 84055 | 47035 | 29741 | 47972 | 61914 | 66864 |
| 436 | 49087 | 61399 | 47781 | 32173 | 96672 | 04528 | 15881 | 46764 | 20115 | 03226 | 79308 | 31970 | 49804 | 85150 |
| 437 | 24808 | 79068 | 70787 | 43106 | 97133 | 37236 | 77888 | 48451 | 20788 | 44648 | 70350 | 64965 | 57715 | 94826 |
| 438 | 89879 | 79942 | 43781 | 05069 | 80143 | 59176 | 47392 | 70372 | 26899 | 16228 | 71205 | 14564 | 97087 | 95690 |
| 439 | 61178 | 79295 | 58926 | 21977 | 28435 | 32631 | 23062 | 31822 | 70462 | 05965 | 22312 | 33013 | 74612 | 23733 |
| 440 | 37444 | 56047 | 23208 | 34710 | 12147 | 28558 | 58817 | 98807 | 56775 | 08129 | 08794 | 23646 | 92846 | 61706 |
| 441 | 99633 | 00363 | 16853 | 20789 | 87674 | 03938 | 36077 | 41012 | 08813 | 51168 | 78822 | 37353 | 61281 | 31172 |
| 442 | 87363 | 59239 | 42023 | 78056 | 51254 | 95644 | 90527 | 41398 | 74996 | 94977 | 22149 | 96616 | 54435 | 52469 |
| 443 | 23923 | 87269 | 85277 | 34727 | 78036 | 74471 | 12157 | 11655 | 25194 | 47557 | 26181 | 67825 | 80224 | 41490 |
| 444 | 45610 | 26370 | 13094 | 34500 | 36750 | 54517 | 85011 | 26567 | 01021 | 32485 | 58903 | 43529 | 24191 | 91832 |
| 445 | 44166 | 80095 | 08286 | 38126 | 48834 | 73423 | 13617 | 08853 | 16286 | 16023 | 77901 | 39118 | 14288 | 39385 |
| 446 | 81875 | 27486 | 53925 | 22330 | 37168 | 97954 | 11967 | 03309 | 97096 | 64221 | 11318 | 98720 | 01100 | 13651 |
| 447 | 79400 | 83852 | 52174 | 42577 | 18553 | 14023 | 69629 | 61913 | 41050 | 69689 | 57284 | 38160 | 57756 | 16762 |
| 448 | 42799 | 46647 | 36718 | 49704 | 17150 | 07935 | 62372 | 39933 | 20838 | 27652 | 54801 | 41067 | 08240 | 35163 |
| 449 | 09302 | 36408 | 64569 | 93033 | 95645 | 56791 | 14830 | 81699 | 45057 | 85796 | 63756 | 93944 | 60649 | 84847 |
| 450 | 88078 | 81456 | 17242 | 84590 | 93660 | 34619 | 51965 | 85618 | 36558 | 54410 | 68456 | 98504 | 83011 | 19393 |

TABLE 1

| Line \ Col. | (1) | (2) | (3) | (4) | (5) | (6) | (7) | (8) | (9) | (10) | (11) | (12) | (13) | (14) |
|---|---|---|---|---|---|---|---|---|---|---|---|---|---|---|
| 451 | 85018 | 23508 | 91507 | 76455 | 54941 | 72711 | 39406 | 94620 | 27963 | 96478 | 21559 | 19246 | 88097 | 44926 |
| 452 | 11904 | 73678 | 08272 | 62941 | 02349 | 71389 | 45605 | 60947 | 60775 | 73181 | 43264 | 56895 | 04232 | 59604 |
| 453 | 75344 | 98489 | 86268 | 73652 | 98210 | 44546 | 27174 | 27499 | 53523 | 63110 | 57106 | 20865 | 91683 | 80688 |
| 454 | 65566 | 65614 | 01443 | 07607 | 11826 | 91326 | 29664 | 01603 | 23156 | 89223 | 43429 | 95353 | 44662 | 59433 |
| 455 | 51872 | 72294 | 95432 | 53555 | 96810 | 17100 | 35066 | 00815 | 01552 | 06392 | 31437 | 70385 | 45863 | 75971 |
| 456 | 03805 | 37913 | 98633 | 81009 | 81060 | 33449 | 68055 | 83844 | 90942 | 74857 | 52419 | 68723 | 47830 | 63010 |
| 457 | 21055 | 78685 | 71250 | 10329 | 56135 | 80647 | 51404 | 06626 | 10042 | 93629 | 37609 | 57215 | 08409 | 81906 |
| 458 | 48977 | 36794 | 56054 | 59843 | 57361 | 65304 | 93258 | 56760 | 63348 | 24949 | 11889 | 29793 | 37457 | 59377 |
| 459 | 93077 | 72941 | 92779 | 23581 | 24548 | 56415 | 61927 | 64416 | 29934 | 00755 | 09418 | 14830 | 62887 | 92683 |
| 460 | 84533 | 26564 | 91583 | 83411 | 66504 | 02036 | 02922 | 63569 | 17906 | 38076 | 32135 | 19096 | 96970 | 75917 |
| 461 | 11338 | 12903 | 14514 | 27585 | 45068 | 05520 | 56321 | 22693 | 35089 | 07694 | 04252 | 23791 | 60249 | 83010 |
| 462 | 23853 | 68500 | 92274 | 87026 | 99717 | 01542 | 72990 | 43413 | 59744 | 44595 | 71326 | 91382 | 45114 | 20245 |
| 463 | 94096 | 74920 | 25822 | 98026 | 05394 | 61840 | 83089 | 09224 | 78530 | 33996 | 49965 | 04851 | 18280 | 14039 |
| 464 | 83160 | 88362 | 09350 | 98536 | 38155 | 42661 | 02363 | 67625 | 34683 | 95372 | 74733 | 63558 | 09665 | 22610 |
| 465 | 97425 | 47335 | 69709 | 01386 | 74319 | 04318 | 99387 | 86874 | 12549 | 38369 | 54952 | 91579 | 26023 | 81076 |
| 466 | 83951 | 11954 | 24317 | 20345 | 18134 | 90062 | 10761 | 54548 | 49505 | 52685 | 63903 | 13193 | 33905 | 66936 |
| 467 | 93085 | 35203 | 05740 | 03206 | 92012 | 42710 | 34650 | 73236 | 66167 | 21788 | 03581 | 40699 | 10396 | 81827 |
| 468 | 33762 | 83193 | 58045 | 89880 | 78101 | 44392 | 53767 | 15220 | 66319 | 72953 | 14071 | 59148 | 95154 | 72852 |
| 469 | 49665 | 85397 | 85137 | 30496 | 23469 | 42846 | 94810 | 16151 | 08029 | 50554 | 03891 | 38313 | 34016 | 18671 |
| 470 | 37541 | 82627 | 80051 | 72521 | 35342 | 56119 | 97190 | 43635 | 84249 | 61254 | 80993 | 55431 | 90793 | 62603 |
| 471 | 22145 | 85304 | 35348 | 82854 | 55846 | 18076 | 12415 | 30193 | 42776 | 85611 | 57635 | 51362 | 79907 | 77364 |
| 472 | 27153 | 08662 | 61078 | 52433 | 22184 | 33998 | 87436 | 37430 | 45246 | 11400 | 20986 | 43996 | 73122 | 88474 |
| 473 | 00301 | 49425 | 66682 | 25442 | 83668 | 66236 | 79655 | 88312 | 93047 | 12088 | 86937 | 70794 | 01041 | 74867 |
| 474 | 43815 | 43272 | 73778 | 63469 | 50083 | 70696 | 13558 | 98995 | 58159 | 04700 | 90443 | 13168 | 31553 | 67891 |
| 475 | 14689 | 86482 | 74157 | 46012 | 97765 | 27552 | 49617 | 51734 | 20849 | 70198 | 67906 | 00880 | 82899 | 66065 |
| 476 | 16680 | 55936 | 82453 | 19538 | 49988 | 13176 | 94219 | 88698 | 41755 | 56216 | 66852 | 17748 | 04963 | 54859 |
| 477 | 86938 | 60429 | 01137 | 86168 | 78257 | 86249 | 46134 | 51865 | 09836 | 73966 | 65711 | 41699 | 11732 | 17173 |
| 478 | 33944 | 29219 | 73161 | 46061 | 30946 | 22210 | 79302 | 40300 | 08852 | 27528 | 84648 | 79589 | 95295 | 72895 |
| 479 | 16045 | 67736 | 18608 | 18198 | 19468 | 76358 | 69203 | 02760 | 28625 | 70476 | 76410 | 32988 | 10194 | 94917 |
| 480 | 37044 | 52523 | 25627 | 63107 | 30806 | 80857 | 84383 | 78450 | 26245 | 91763 | 73117 | 33047 | 03577 | 62599 |
| 481 | 61471 | 45322 | 35340 | 35132 | 42163 | 69332 | 98851 | 50252 | 56911 | 62693 | 73817 | 98693 | 18728 | 94741 |
| 482 | 47422 | 21296 | 16785 | 66393 | 39249 | 51463 | 95963 | 07929 | 66728 | 47761 | 81472 | 44806 | 15592 | 71357 |
| 483 | 24133 | 39719 | 14484 | 58613 | 88717 | 29289 | 77360 | 09030 | 39605 | 87507 | 85446 | 51257 | 89555 | 75520 |
| 484 | 67253 | 67064 | 10748 | 16006 | 16767 | 57345 | 42285 | 56670 | 88445 | 85799 | 76200 | 21795 | 38894 | 58070 |
| 485 | 62382 | 76941 | 01635 | 35829 | 77516 | 98468 | 51686 | 48140 | 13583 | 94911 | 13318 | 64741 | 64336 | 95103 |
| 486 | 98011 | 16503 | 09201 | 03523 | 87192 | 66483 | 55649 | 36764 | 86132 | 12463 | 28385 | 94242 | 32063 | 45233 |
| 487 | 37366 | 24386 | 20654 | 85117 | 74078 | 64120 | 04643 | 14351 | 71381 | 28133 | 68269 | 65145 | 28152 | 39087 |
| 488 | 73587 | 83993 | 54176 | 05221 | 94119 | 20108 | 78101 | 81276 | 00835 | 63835 | 87174 | 42446 | 08882 | 27067 |
| 489 | 33583 | 68291 | 50547 | 96085 | 62180 | 27453 | 18567 | 55524 | 86088 | 00069 | 59254 | 24654 | 77371 | 26409 |
| 490 | 02878 | 33223 | 39199 | 49536 | 56199 | 05993 | 71201 | 78852 | 65889 | 32719 | 13758 | 23937 | 90740 | 16866 |
| 491 | 91498 | 41673 | 17195 | 33175 | 04994 | 09879 | 70337 | 11861 | 69032 | 51915 | 23510 | 32050 | 52052 | 24004 |
| 492 | 91127 | 19815 | 30219 | 55591 | 21725 | 43827 | 78862 | 67699 | 01009 | 07050 | 73324 | 06732 | 27510 | 33761 |
| 493 | 12997 | 55013 | 18662 | 81724 | 24305 | 37661 | 18956 | 50064 | 39500 | 17450 | 18030 | 63124 | 48061 | 59412 |
| 494 | 96098 | 13651 | 15393 | 69995 | 14762 | 69734 | 89150 | 93126 | 17700 | 94400 | 76075 | 08317 | 27324 | 72723 |
| 495 | 97627 | 17837 | 10472 | 18983 | 26387 | 99781 | 52977 | 01657 | 92602 | 41043 | 05686 | 15650 | 29970 | 95877 |
| 496 | 40064 | 47981 | 31484 | 76603 | 54088 | 91095 | 00010 | 13800 | 76690 | 75133 | 60455 | 28491 | 03845 | 11507 |
| 497 | 16239 | 68743 | 71374 | 55863 | 22672 | 91609 | 51514 | 98135 | 42870 | 48578 | 29036 | 69876 | 86563 | 61729 |
| 498 | 58354 | 24913 | 20435 | 30965 | 17453 | 65623 | 93058 | 08313 | 99293 | 00990 | 13595 | 77457 | 79969 | 11339 |
| 499 | 52567 | 65085 | 60220 | 84641 | 18273 | 49604 | 47418 | 90974 | 83965 | 62732 | 85161 | 54330 | 22406 | 86253 |
| 500 | 06236 | 29052 | 91392 | 07551 | 83532 | 68130 | 56970 | 33273 | 61993 | 88407 | 69399 | 17301 | 70975 | 99129 |

## SAMPLE SIZES FOR SAMPLING ATTRIBUTES
## FOR RANDOM SAMPLES ONLY

**TABLE 2a** *Expected Rate of Occurrence not over 10%*
*Confidence Level 95%*

| *Number of Items in Field* | ± 1% | ± 2% | ± 3% | ± 4% | ± 5% |
|---|---|---|---|---|---|
| | *Sample Size for Reliability of:* | | | | |
| 200 | | | | 104 | 82 |
| 300 | | | | 126 | 95 |
| 400 | | | 196 | 140 | 103 |
| 500 | | | 217 | 151 | 108 |
| 1,000 | | 464 | 277 | 178 | 121 |
| 1,500 | | 548 | 306 | 189 | 127 |
| 2,000 | | 603 | 322 | 195 | 129 |
| 2,500 | | 642 | 333 | 199 | 131 |
| 3,000 | | 671 | 340 | 201 | 132 |
| 3,500 | 1739 | 693 | 346 | 203 | 133 |
| 4,000 | 1854 | 711 | 350 | 205 | 134 |
| 4,500 | 1955 | 725 | 354 | 206 | 134 |
| 5,000 | 2044 | 737 | 357 | 207 | 135 |
| 6,000 | 2193 | 755 | 361 | 208 | 135 |
| 7,000 | 2314 | 769 | 364 | 210 | 136 |
| 8,000 | 2413 | 780 | 366 | 210 | 136 |
| 9,000 | 2497 | 788 | 368 | 211 | 136 |
| 10,000 | 2568 | 795 | 370 | 211 | 136 |
| 15,000 | 2809 | 817 | 374 | 213 | 137 |
| 20,000 | 2947 | 828 | 377 | 214 | 137 |
| 25,000 | 3036 | 835 | 378 | 214 | 137 |
| 50,000 | 3233 | 849 | 381 | 215 | 138 |
| 100,000 | 3341 | 857 | 383 | 216 | 138 |

**TABLE 2b** *Expected Rate of Occurrence not over 10%*
*Confidence Level 99%*

| *Number of Items in Field* | ± 1% | ± 2% | ± 3% | ± 4% | ± 5% | ± 10% |
|---|---|---|---|---|---|---|
| | *Sample Size for Reliability of:* | | | | | |
| 200 | | | | | | 46 |
| 300 | | | | | 133 | 50 |
| 400 | | | | 193 | 150 | 52 |
| 500 | | | | 214 | 162 | 53 |
| 1,000 | | | 399 | 272 | 193 | 56 |
| 1,500 | | | 460 | 299 | 206 | 57 |
| 2,000 | | 855 | 498 | 315 | 213 | 58 |
| 2,500 | | 935 | 525 | 325 | 218 | 59 |
| 3,000 | | 997 | 544 | 332 | 221 | 59 |
| 3,500 | | 1047 | 558 | 337 | 224 | 59 |
| 4,000 | | 1087 | 569 | 341 | 225 | 59 |
| 4,500 | | 1121 | 578 | 345 | 227 | 59 |
| 5,000 | | 1150 | 586 | 347 | 228 | 59 |
| 6,000 | 2993 | 1196 | 598 | 351 | 230 | 59 |
| 7,000 | 3223 | 1231 | 606 | 354 | 231 | 59 |
| 8,000 | 3420 | 1258 | 613 | 357 | 232 | 59 |
| 9,000 | 3590 | 1281 | 618 | 358 | 233 | 59 |
| 10,000 | 3739 | 1299 | 622 | 360 | 233 | 59 |
| 15,000 | 4272 | 1358 | 635 | 364 | 235 | 59 |
| 20,000 | 4599 | 1389 | 642 | 366 | 236 | 60 |
| 25,000 | 4821 | 1409 | 646 | 368 | 237 | 60 |
| 50,000 | 5332 | 1450 | 655 | 371 | 238 | 60 |
| 100,000 | 5636 | 1471 | 659 | 372 | 238 | 60 |

**TABLE 2c**

## SAMPLE SIZES FOR SAMPLING ATTRIBUTES
## FOR RANDOM SAMPLES ONLY

*Expected Rate of Occurrence not over 5%*
*Confidence Level 95%*

| *Number of Items in Field* | ± 1% | *Sample Size for Reliability of:* ± 2% | ± 3% | ± 4% |
|---|---|---|---|---|
| 200 | | | 101 | 73 |
| 300 | | | 121 | 83 |
| 400 | | | 135 | 89 |
| 500 | | 238 | 144 | 93 |
| 1,000 | | 313 | 169 | 102 |
| 1,500 | | 350 | 179 | 106 |
| 2,000 | 954 | 371 | 184 | 108 |
| 2,500 | 1055 | 386 | 187 | 109 |
| 3,000 | 1134 | 396 | 190 | 110 |
| 3,500 | 1199 | 403 | 192 | 110 |
| 4,000 | 1253 | 409 | 193 | 111 |
| 4,500 | 1298 | 414 | 194 | 111 |
| 5,000 | 1336 | 418 | 195 | 111 |
| 6,000 | 1399 | 424 | 196 | 112 |
| 7,000 | 1447 | 428 | 197 | 112 |
| 8,000 | 1485 | 431 | 198 | 112 |
| 9,000 | 1517 | 434 | 198 | 113 |
| 10,000 | 1543 | 436 | 199 | 113 |
| 15,000 | 1626 | 443 | 200 | 113 |
| 20,000 | 1672 | 446 | 201 | 113 |
| 25,000 | 1700 | 448 | 201 | 113 |
| 50,000 | 1760 | 452 | 202 | 114 |
| 100,000 | 1791 | 454 | 202 | 114 |

**TABLE 2d**

*Expected Rate of Occurrence not over 5%*
*Confidence Level 99%*

| *Number of Items in Field* | ± 1% | *Sample Size for Reliability of:* ± 2% | ± 3% | ± 4% | ± 5% |
|---|---|---|---|---|---|
| 200 | | | | 99 | 78 |
| 300 | | | | 119 | 89 |
| 400 | | | 187 | 132 | 96 |
| 500 | | | 206 | 142 | 101 |
| 1,000 | | 441 | 260 | 165 | 112 |
| 1,500 | | 517 | 284 | 174 | 117 |
| 2,000 | | 565 | 298 | 179 | 119 |
| 2,500 | | 599 | 307 | 183 | 120 |
| 3,000 | | 624 | 314 | 185 | 121 |
| 3,500 | 1659 | 643 | 318 | 187 | 122 |
| 4,000 | 1763 | 658 | 322 | 188 | 122 |
| 4,500 | 1858 | 673 | 326 | 189 | 123 |
| 5,000 | 1934 | 681 | 327 | 190 | 123 |
| 6,000 | 2067 | 697 | 331 | 191 | 124 |
| 7,000 | 2174 | 708 | 334 | 192 | 124 |
| 8,000 | 2261 | 717 | 336 | 192 | 124 |
| 9,000 | 2335 | 725 | 337 | 193 | 124 |
| 10,000 | 2397 | 731 | 338 | 193 | 125 |
| 15,000 | 2605 | 749 | 342 | 194 | 125 |
| 20,000 | 2721 | 758 | 344 | 195 | 125 |
| 25,000 | 2799 | 764 | 345 | 195 | 126 |
| 50,000 | 2963 | 776 | 348 | 196 | 126 |
| 100,000 | 3056 | 782 | 349 | 197 | 126 |

TABLE 2e

## SAMPLE SIZES FOR SAMPLING ATTRIBUTES

### FOR RANDOM SAMPLES ONLY

*Expected Rate of Occurrence not over 2%*
*Confidence Level 95%*

| *Number of Items in Field* | ± .5% | *Sample Size for Reliability of:* ± 1% | ± 2% | ± 3% |
|---|---|---|---|---|
| 200 | | | 97 | 59 |
| 300 | | | 116 | 66 |
| 400 | | | 128 | 70 |
| 500 | | | 137 | 72 |
| 1,000 | | 430 | 158 | 78 |
| 1,500 | | 501 | 167 | 80 |
| 2,000 | | 547 | 172 | 81 |
| 2,500 | | 579 | 175 | 81 |
| 3,000 | 1503 | 602 | 177 | 82 |
| 3,500 | 1619 | 620 | 179 | 82 |
| 4,000 | 1718 | 634 | 180 | 82 |
| 4,500 | 1804 | 645 | 181 | 83 |
| 5,000 | 1880 | 654 | 182 | 83 |
| 6,000 | 2005 | 669 | 183 | 83 |
| 7,000 | 2106 | 680 | 183 | 83 |
| 8,000 | 2188 | 688 | 184 | 83 |
| 9,000 | 2257 | 695 | 184 | 83 |
| 10,000 | 2315 | 700 | 185 | 83 |
| 15,000 | 2508 | 717 | 186 | 84 |
| 20,000 | 2664 | 726 | 186 | 84 |
| 25,000 | 2688 | 731 | 187 | 84 |
| 50,000 | 2840 | 742 | 188 | 84 |
| 100,000 | 2924 | 747 | 188 | 84 |

TABLE 2f

*Expected Rate of Occurrence not over 2%*
*Confidence Level 99%*

| *Number of Items in Field* | ± .5% | *Sample Size for Reliability of:* ± 1% | ± 2% | ± 3% |
|---|---|---|---|---|
| 200 | | | | 84 |
| 300 | | | | 98 |
| 400 | | | 180 | 107 |
| 500 | | | 197 | 113 |
| 1,000 | | | 246 | 127 |
| 1,500 | | 697 | 268 | 132 |
| 2,000 | | 788 | 280 | 135 |
| 2,500 | | 856 | 289 | 137 |
| 3,000 | | 907 | 294 | 138 |
| 3,500 | | 948 | 298 | 139 |
| 4,000 | | 981 | 301 | 140 |
| 4,500 | | 1009 | 304 | 140 |
| 5,000 | | 1032 | 306 | 141 |
| 6,000 | 2786 | 1069 | 309 | 142 |
| 7,000 | 2984 | 1097 | 311 | 142 |
| 8,000 | 3151 | 1118 | 313 | 142 |
| 9,000 | 3296 | 1136 | 314 | 143 |
| 10,000 | 3421 | 1151 | 315 | 143 |
| 15,000 | 3861 | 1197 | 319 | 144 |
| 20,000 | 4126 | 1221 | 320 | 144 |
| 25,000 | 4304 | 1236 | 321 | 144 |
| 50,000 | 4709 | 1267 | 323 | 144 |
| 100,000 | 4942 | 1283 | 324 | 145 |

**TABLE 2g** SAMPLE SIZES FOR SAMPLING ATTRIBUTES

**FOR RANDOM SAMPLES ONLY**

*Expected Rate of Occurrence Unknown (50%)*
*Confidence Level 95%*

| *Number of Items in Field* | ± 2% | *Sample Size for Reliability of:* ± 3% | ± 4% | ± 5% |
|---|---|---|---|---|
| 200 | | | | |
| 300 | | | | |
| 400 | | | | 196 |
| 500 | | | | 217 |
| 1,000 | | | 375 | 278 |
| 1,500 | | 624 | 429 | 306 |
| 2,000 | | 696 | 462 | 322 |
| 2,500 | 1225 | 748 | 484 | 333 |
| 3,000 | 1334 | 787 | 500 | 341 |
| 3,500 | 1424 | 818 | 512 | 346 |
| 4,000 | 1500 | 842 | 522 | 350 |
| 4,500 | 1566 | 863 | 530 | 354 |
| 5,000 | 1622 | 879 | 536 | 357 |
| 6,000 | 1715 | 906 | 546 | 361 |
| 7,000 | 1788 | 926 | 553 | 364 |
| 8,000 | 1847 | 942 | 558 | 367 |
| 9,000 | 1895 | 954 | 563 | 368 |
| 10,000 | 1936 | 964 | 566 | 370 |
| 15,000 | 2070 | 996 | 577 | 375 |
| 20,000 | 2144 | 1013 | 583 | 377 |
| 25,000 | 2191 | 1023 | 586 | 378 |
| 50,000 | 2291 | 1045 | 593 | 381 |
| 100,000 | 2345 | 1056 | 597 | 383 |

**TABLE 2h** *Expected Rate of Occurrence Unknown (50%)*
*Confidence Level 99%*

| *Number of Items in Field* | ± 2% | *Sample Size for Reliability of:* ± 3% | ± 4% | ± 5% | ± 10% |
|---|---|---|---|---|---|
| 200 | | | | | 91 |
| 300 | | | | | 107 |
| 400 | | | | | 118 |
| 500 | | | | | 125 |
| 1,000 | | | | 400 | 143 |
| 1,500 | | | 613 | 460 | 150 |
| 2,000 | | 959 | 683 | 498 | 154 |
| 2,500 | | 1061 | 733 | 525 | 156 |
| 3,000 | | 1142 | 771 | 544 | 158 |
| 3,500 | | 1210 | 802 | 559 | 159 |
| 4,000 | | 1262 | 824 | 569 | 160 |
| 4,500 | 2158 | 1308 | 843 | 578 | 160 |
| 5,000 | 2267 | 1347 | 859 | 586 | 161 |
| 6,000 | 2452 | 1410 | 884 | 598 | 162 |
| 7,000 | 2605 | 1459 | 903 | 606 | 162 |
| 8,000 | 2732 | 1498 | 918 | 613 | 163 |
| 9,000 | 2839 | 1530 | 930 | 618 | 163 |
| 10,000 | 2932 | 1556 | 939 | 622 | 164 |
| 15,000 | 3249 | 1642 | 970 | 635 | 164 |
| 20,000 | 3435 | 1688 | 986 | 642 | 165 |
| 25,000 | 3557 | 1717 | 996 | 646 | 165 |
| 50,000 | 3830 | 1778 | 1016 | 655 | 166 |
| 100,000 | 3982 | 1810 | 1026 | 659 | 166 |

**NOTE: This table should be used only when the auditor is unable or unwilling to fix a maximum occurrence rate to be expected. This conservative approach will result in a *much* larger sample size than will be found in the other tables (tables 2a thru 2f) where an expected maximum rate is estimated. The tables are based on an assumption of an occurrence rate of 50%.**

## TABLE 3

### FACTORS FOR ESTIMATING THE STANDARD DEVIATION

$$\text{Estimated Standard Deviation} = \frac{\text{Average Range}}{d_2 \text{ Factor}}$$

| Group Size | $d_2$ Factor |
|---|---|
| 5 | 2.326 |
| 6 | 2.534 |
| 7 | 2.704 |
| 8 | 2.847 |

## TABLE 4

## SAMPLE SIZES FOR ESTIMATING AVERAGE VALUES FOR RANDOM SAMPLES ONLY

| *Ratio of Sampling Error to Standard Deviation (Sampling Error/Standard Deviation)* | *Sample Size Required With Confidence Levels of* 95% | 99% | 99.9% |
|---|---|---|---|
| *Field Size is 500* | | | |
| .10 | 217 | — | — |
| .15 | 127 | 186 | 246 |
| .20 | 81 | 125 | 176 |
| .25 | 55 | 88 | 129 |
| .30 | 39 | 65 | 97 |
| *Field Size is 1000* | | | |
| .10 | 278 | 399 | — |
| .15 | 146 | 228 | 326 |
| .20 | 88 | 143 | 314 |
| .25 | 58 | 96 | 148 |
| .30 | 41 | 69 | 108 |
| *Field Size is 2000* | | | |
| .05 | 869 | — | — |
| .10 | 322 | 499 | 705 |
| .15 | 157 | 258 | 390 |
| .20 | 92 | 154 | 240 |
| .25 | 60 | 101 | 160 |
| .30 | 42 | 72 | 114 |
| *Field Size is 3000* | | | |
| .05 | 1016 | 1409 | — |
| .10 | 341 | 544 | 799 |
| .15 | 162 | 269 | 417 |
| .20 | 93 | 158 | 250 |
| .25 | 60 | 103 | 165 |
| .30 | 42 | 72 | 116 |
| *Field Size is 4000* | | | |
| .04 | 1500 | — | — |
| .05 | 1110 | 1596 | — |
| .10 | 351 | 570 | 856 |
| .15 | 164 | 275 | 432 |
| .20 | 94 | 160 | 255 |
| .25 | 61 | 104 | 167 |
| .30 | 42 | 73 | 117 |
| *Field Size is 5000* | | | |
| .03 | 2303 | — | — |
| .04 | 1622 | 2267 | — |
| .05 | 1175 | 1734 | 2328 |
| .10 | 357 | 586 | 894 |
| .15 | 165 | 279 | 441 |
| .20 | 94 | 161 | 258 |
| .25 | 61 | 104 | 168 |
| .30 | 42 | 73 | 118 |

## SAMPLE SIZES FOR ESTIMATING AVERAGE VALUES
## FOR RANDOM SAMPLES ONLY

| *Ratio of Sampling Error to Standard Deviation (Sampling Error/Standard Deviation)* | *Sample Size Required With Confidence Levels of* 95% | 99% | 99.9% |
|---|---|---|---|
| *Field Size is 10,000* | | | |
| .03 | 2991 | 4244 | — |
| .04 | 1936 | 2932 | 4050 |
| .05 | 1332 | 2098 | 3034 |
| .10 | 370 | 623 | 982 |
| .15 | 168 | 287 | 462 |
| .20 | 95 | 164 | 265 |
| .25 | 61 | 106 | 171 |
| .30 | 43 | 74 | 120 |
| *Field Size is 20,000* | | | |
| .02 | 6489 | 9068 | — |
| .03 | 3517 | 5388 | 7541 |
| .04 | 2144 | 3436 | 5079 |
| .05 | 1427 | 2344 | 3577 |
| .10 | 377 | 643 | 1033 |
| .15 | 169 | 291 | 473 |
| .20 | 96 | 165 | 269 |
| .25 | 61 | 106 | 173 |
| .30 | 43 | 74 | 120 |
| *Field Size is 100,000 and up* | | | |
| .01 | 27755 | 39889 | — |
| .02 | 8764 | 14229 | 21413 |
| .03 | 4093 | 6867 | 10799 |
| .04 | 2345 | 3983 | 6373 |
| .05 | 1513 | 2586 | 4174 |
| .10 | 383 | 660 | 1077 |
| .15 | 170 | 295 | 482 |
| .20 | 96 | 166 | 272 |
| .25 | 61 | 107 | 174 |
| .30 | 43 | 74 | 121 |

## TABLE 5

### PROBABILITIES OF INCLUDING *AT LEAST ONE* OCCURRENCE IN A SAMPLE

### FOR RANDOM SAMPLES ONLY

| *When Sample Size is:* | *When Occurrence Rate is:* *.05%* | *.1%* | *.5%* | *1%* | *2%* | *5%* | *10%* |
|---|---|---|---|---|---|---|---|
| | *Probability of finding at least one occurrence is:* | | | | | | |
| | ***Field Size is 200*** | | | | | | |
| 10 | | | | 9.8% | 18.7% | 40.9% | 66.0% |
| 25 | | | | 23.5 | 41.6 | 74.6 | 94.0 |
| 40 | | | | 36.1 | 59.4 | 89.9 | 99.1 |
| 50 | | | | 43.8 | 68.7 | 94.8 | 99.8 |
| 60 | | | | 51.1 | 76.3 | 97.4 | 99.9 |
| 80 | | | | 64.1 | 87.3 | 99.5 | 100.0 |
| | ***Field Size is 500*** | | | | | | |
| 10 | | | 5.9% | 9.6% | 18.4% | 40.4% | 65.5% |
| 25 | | | 14.3 | 22.7 | 40.4 | 73.2 | 93.3 |
| 50 | | | 27.1 | 41.1 | 65.5 | 93.3 | 99.6 |
| 75 | | | 38.7 | 55.8 | 80.6 | 98.5 | 100.0 |
| 100 | | | 48.9 | 67.4 | 89.5 | 99.7 | 100.0 |
| 200 | | | 78.5 | 92.3 | 99.4 | 100.0 | 100.0 |
| | ***Field Size is 1000*** | | | | | | |
| 10 | | 1.0% | 4.9% | 9.6% | 18.4% | 40.3% | 65.3% |
| 25 | | 2.5 | 11.9 | 22.5 | 40.0 | 72.7 | 93.1 |
| 50 | | 5.0 | 22.7 | 40.3 | 64.5 | 92.8 | 99.6 |
| 100 | | 10.0 | 41.0 | 65.3 | 88.1 | 99.6 | 100.0 |
| 200 | | 20.0 | 67.3 | 89.4 | 98.9 | 100.0 | 100.0 |
| 400 | | 40.0 | 92.3 | 99.4 | 100.0 | 100.0 | 100.0 |
| | ***Field Size is 2000*** | | | | | | |
| 10 | 0.5% | 1.0% | 4.9% | 9.6% | 18.3% | 40.2% | 65.2% |
| 50 | 2.5 | 4.9 | 22.4 | 39.9 | 64.0 | 92.6 | 99.5 |
| 100 | 5.0 | 9.8 | 40.2 | 64.3 | 87.4 | 99.5 | 100.0 |
| 200 | 10.0 | 19.0 | 65.2 | 88.0 | 98.6 | 100.0 | 100.0 |
| 400 | 20.0 | 36.0 | 89.3 | 98.9 | 100.0 | 100.0 | 100.0 |
| 600 | 30.0 | 51.0 | 97.2 | 99.9 | 100.0 | 100.0 | 100.0 |

## PROBABILITIES OF INCLUDING AT LEAST ONE OCCURRENCE IN A SAMPLE

## FOR RANDOM SAMPLES ONLY

| *When Sample Size is:* | *When Occurrence Rate is:* .05% | .1% | .5% | 1% | 2% | 5% | 10% |
|---|---|---|---|---|---|---|---|
| | *Probability of finding at least one occurrence is:* | | | | | | |
| | *Field Size is 3000* | | | | | | |
| 10 | 0.5% | 1.0% | 4.9% | 9.6% | 18.3% | 40.2% | 65.2% |
| 100 | 5.0 | 9.7 | 39.3 | 64.0 | 87.2 | 99.5 | 100.0 |
| 200 | 9.8 | 18.7 | 64.6 | 87.5 | 98.5 | 100.0 | 100.0 |
| 400 | 19.3 | 34.9 | 88.4 | 98.7 | 100.0 | 100.0 | 100.0 |
| 600 | 28.4 | 48.8 | 96.5 | 99.9 | 100.0 | 100.0 | 100.0 |
| 800 | 37.2 | 60.6 | 99.1 | 100.0 | 100.0 | 100.0 | 100.0 |
| 1000 | 45.6 | 70.4 | 99.8 | 100.0 | 100.0 | 100.0 | 100.0 |
| | *Field Size is 10,000* | | | | | | |
| 100 | 4.9% | 9.6% | 39.6% | 63.6% | 86.9% | | |
| 200 | 9.6 | 18.3 | 63.7 | 86.9 | 98.3 | | |
| 500 | 22.6 | 40.1 | 92.4 | 99.4 | 100.0 | | |
| 1000 | 41.0 | 65.1 | 99.5 | 100.0 | 100.0 | | |
| | *Field Size is 15,000* | | | | | | |
| 100 | 4.9% | 9.6% | 39.5% | 63.5% | 86.8% | | |
| 200 | 9.6 | 18.2 | 63.4 | 86.8 | 98.3 | | |
| 500 | 22.4 | 39.9 | 92.2 | 99.4 | 100.0 | | |
| 1000 | 40.4 | 64.5 | 99.4 | 100.0 | 100.0 | | |
| | *Field Size is 40,000* | | | | | | |
| 100 | 4.9% | 9.5% | 39.5% | 63.4% | 86.8% | | |
| 200 | 9.6 | 18.2 | 63.4 | 86.7 | 98.3 | | |
| 500 | 22.2 | 39.6 | 92.0 | 99.4 | 100.0 | | |
| 1000 | 39.7 | 63.7 | 99.4 | 100.0 | 100.0 | | |
| | *Field Size is 100,000* | | | | | | |
| 100 | 4.9% | 9.5% | 39.4% | 63.4% | 86.8% | | |
| 200 | 9.5 | 18.2 | 63.3 | 86.7 | 98.2 | | |
| 500 | 22.2 | 39.5 | 91.9 | 99.3 | 100.0 | | |
| 1000 | 39.5 | 63.4 | 99.3 | 100.0 | 100.0 | | |

## SAMPLE RELIABILITY FOR RELATIVE FREQUENCIES
## FOR RANDOM SAMPLES ONLY

*Rate of Occurrence in Sample 1%*
*Confidence Level 95%*

| | *For Sample Size of:* | | | | | | | | | | | |
|---|---|---|---|---|---|---|---|---|---|---|---|---|
| | 100 | | 200 | | 300 | | 500 | | 1000 | | 2000 | |
| *And Field Size is:* | *Lower Limit* | *Upper Limit* | *Lower Limit* | *Upper Limit* | *Lower Limit* | *Upper Limit* | *Lower Limit* | *Upper Limit* | *Lower Limit* | *Upper Limit* | *Lower Limit* | *Upper Limit* |
| 200 | 0.3% | 4.2% | | | | | | | | | | |
| 300 | 0.2 | 4.6 | | | | | | | | | | |
| 400 | 0.2 | 4.9 | 0.4% | 2.8% | | | | | | | | |
| 500 | 0.1 | 5.0 | 0.3 | 3.0 | | | | | | | | |
| 1,000 | 0.1 | 5.2 | 0.2 | 3.3 | 0.3% | 2.6% | 0.5% | 1.9% | | | | |
| 1,500 | 0.1 | 5.3 | 0.2 | 3.4 | 0.3 | 2.7 | 0.5 | 2.1 | | | | |
| 2,000 | 0.1 | 5.3 | 0.2 | 3.4 | 0.3 | 2.8 | 0.4 | 2.1 | 0.6% | 1.6% | | |
| 2,500 | 0.0* | 5.4 | 0.2 | 3.5 | 0.3 | 2.8 | 0.4 | 2.2 | 0.6 | 1.6 | | |
| 3,000 | 0.0* | 5.4 | 0.2 | 3.5 | 0.3 | 2.8 | 0.4 | 2.2 | 0.6 | 1.7 | | |
| 3,500 | 0.0* | 5.4 | 0.2 | 3.5 | 0.2 | 2.8 | 0.4 | 2.2 | 0.6 | 1.7 | | |
| 4,000 | 0.0* | 5.4 | 0.1 | 3.5 | 0.2 | 2.8 | 0.4 | 2.2 | 0.6 | 1.7 | 0.7% | 1.4% |
| 4,500 | 0.0* | 5.4 | 0.1 | 3.5 | 0.2 | 2.8 | 0.4 | 2.2 | 0.5 | 1.7 | 0.7 | 1.4 |
| 5,000 | 0.0* | 5.4 | 0.1 | 3.5 | 0.2 | 2.8 | 0.4 | 2.3 | 0.5 | 1.7 | 0.7 | 1.4 |
| 6,000 | 0.0* | 5.4 | 0.1 | 3.5 | 0.2 | 2.9 | 0.4 | 2.3 | 0.5 | 1.8 | 0.7 | 1.4 |
| 7,000 | 0.0* | 5.4 | 0.1 | 3.5 | 0.2 | 2.9 | 0.4 | 2.3 | 0.5 | 1.8 | 0.7 | 1.5 |
| 8,000 | 0.0* | 5.4 | 0.1 | 3.5 | 0.2 | 2.9 | 0.4 | 2.3 | 0.5 | 1.8 | 0.7 | 1.5 |
| 9,000 | 0.0* | 5.4 | 0.1 | 3.5 | 0.2 | 2.9 | 0.3 | 2.3 | 0.5 | 1.8 | 0.7 | 1.5 |
| 10,000 | 0.0* | 5.4 | 0.1 | 3.5 | 0.2 | 2.9 | 0.3 | 2.3 | 0.5 | 1.8 | 0.7 | 1.5 |
| 15,000 | 0.0* | 5.4 | 0.1 | 3.6 | 0.2 | 2.9 | 0.3 | 2.3 | 0.5 | 1.8 | 0.6 | 1.5 |
| 20,000 | 0.0* | 5.4 | 0.1 | 3.6 | 0.2 | 2.9 | 0.3 | 2.3 | 0.5 | 1.8 | 0.6 | 1.5 |
| 25,000 | 0.0* | 5.4 | 0.1 | 3.6 | 0.2 | 2.9 | 0.3 | 2.3 | 0.5 | 1.8 | 0.6 | 1.5 |
| 50,000 | 0.0* | 5.5 | 0.1 | 3.6 | 0.2 | 2.9 | 0.3 | 2.3 | 0.5 | 1.8 | 0.6 | 1.5 |
| 100,000 | 0.0* | 5.5 | 0.1 | 3.6 | 0.2 | 2.9 | 0.3 | 2.3 | 0.5 | 1.8 | 0.6 | 1.5 |

* Less than 0.05%

## SAMPLE RELIABILITY FOR RELATIVE FREQUENCIES

## FOR RANDOM SAMPLES ONLY

*Rate of Occurrence in Sample 2%*
*Confidence Level 95%*

| *And Field Size is:* | *For Sample Size of:* 50 *Lower Limit* | 50 *Upper Limit* | 100 *Lower Limit* | 100 *Upper Limit* | 200 *Lower Limit* | 200 *Upper Limit* | 300 *Lower Limit* | 300 *Upper Limit* | 500 *Lower Limit* | 500 *Upper Limit* | 1000 *Lower Limit* | 1000 *Upper Limit* | 2000 *Lower Limit* | 2000 *Upper Limit* |
|---|---|---|---|---|---|---|---|---|---|---|---|---|---|---|
| 200 | 0.3% | 9.5% | 0.8% | 5.6% | | | | | | | | | | |
| 300 | 0.2 | 9.9 | 0.6 | 6.1 | | | | | | | | | | |
| 400 | 0.2 | 10.1 | 0.5 | 6.4 | 1.0% | 4.2% | | | | | | | | |
| 500 | 0.2 | 10.2 | 0.4 | 6.5 | 0.9 | 4.4 | | | | | | | | |
| 1,000 | 0.1 | 10.4 | 0.3 | 6.8 | 0.7 | 4.7 | 1.1% | 3.8% | 1.3% | 3.1% | | | | |
| 1,500 | 0.1 | 10.5 | 0.3 | 6.9 | 0.7 | 4.8 | 1.0 | 4.0 | 1.2 | 3.3 | | | | |
| 2,000 | 0.1 | 10.6 | 0.3 | 6.9 | 0.6 | 4.9 | 1.0 | 4.0 | 1.2 | 3.4 | 1.5% | 2.7% | | |
| 2,500 | 0.1 | 10.6 | 0.3 | 6.9 | 0.6 | 4.9 | 0.9 | 4.1 | 1.2 | 3.4 | 1.5 | 2.8 | | |
| 3,000 | 0.1 | 10.6 | 0.3 | 7.0 | 0.6 | 4.9 | 0.9 | 4.1 | 1.1 | 3.4 | 1.4 | 2.8 | | |
| 3,500 | 0.1 | 10.6 | 0.3 | 7.0 | 0.6 | 5.0 | 0.9 | 4.1 | 1.1 | 3.4 | 1.4 | 2.9 | | |
| 4,000 | 0.1 | 10.6 | 0.3 | 7.0 | 0.6 | 5.0 | 0.9 | 4.1 | 1.1 | 3.5 | 1.4 | 2.9 | 1.6% | 2.5% |
| 4,500 | 0.1 | 10.6 | 0.3 | 7.0 | 0.6 | 5.0 | 0.9 | 4.1 | 1.1 | 3.5 | 1.4 | 2.9 | 1.6 | 2.5 |
| 5,000 | 0.1 | 10.6 | 0.3 | 7.0 | 0.6 | 5.0 | 0.9 | 4.1 | 1.1 | 3.5 | 1.4 | 2.9 | 1.6 | 2.5 |
| 6,000 | 0.1 | 10.6 | 0.3 | 7.0 | 0.6 | 5.0 | 0.9 | 4.1 | 1.1 | 3.5 | 1.4 | 2.9 | 1.6 | 2.6 |
| 7,000 | 0.1 | 10.6 | 0.3 | 7.0 | 0.6 | 5.0 | 0.9 | 4.2 | 1.1 | 3.5 | 1.3 | 2.9 | 1.6 | 2.6 |
| 8,000 | 0.1 | 10.6 | 0.3 | 7.0 | 0.6 | 5.0 | 0.9 | 4.2 | 1.1 | 3.5 | 1.3 | 2.9 | 1.6 | 2.6 |
| 9,000 | 0.1 | 10.6 | 0.3 | 7.0 | 0.6 | 5.0 | 0.9 | 4.2 | 1.1 | 3.5 | 1.3 | 3.0 | 1.5 | 2.6 |
| 10,000 | 0.1 | 10.6 | 0.3 | 7.0 | 0.6 | 5.0 | 0.9 | 4.2 | 1.1 | 3.5 | 1.3 | 3.0 | 1.5 | 2.6 |
| 15,000 | 0.1 | 10.7 | 0.3 | 7.0 | 0.6 | 5.0 | 0.9 | 4.2 | 1.1 | 3.5 | 1.3 | 3.0 | 1.5 | 2.6 |
| 20,000 | 0.1 | 10.7 | 0.2 | 7.0 | 0.6 | 5.0 | 0.9 | 4.2 | 1.1 | 3.5 | 1.3 | 3.0 | 1.5 | 2.6 |
| 25,000 | 0.1 | 10.7 | 0.2 | 7.0 | 0.6 | 5.0 | 0.9 | 4.2 | 1.1 | 3.5 | 1.3 | 3.0 | 1.5 | 2.6 |
| 50,000 | 0.1 | 10.7 | 0.2 | 7.0 | 0.6 | 5.0 | 0.9 | 4.2 | 1.1 | 3.6 | 1.3 | 3.0 | 1.5 | 2.7 |
| 100,000 | 0.1 | 10.7 | 0.2 | 7.0 | 0.6 | 5.0 | 0.9 | 4.2 | 1.1 | 3.6 | 1.3 | 3.0 | 1.5 | 2.7 |

TABLE 6 (Continued)

## SAMPLE RELIABILITY FOR RELATIVE FREQUENCIES FOR RANDOM SAMPLES ONLY

*Rate of Occurrence in Sample 3%*
*Confidence Level 95%*

*For Sample Size of:*

| *And Field Size is:* | 100 *Lower Limit* | 100 *Upper Limit* | 200 *Lower Limit* | 200 *Upper Limit* | 300 *Lower Limit* | 300 *Upper Limit* | 500 *Lower Limit* | 500 *Upper Limit* | 1000 *Lower Limit* | 1000 *Upper Limit* | 2000 *Lower Limit* | 2000 *Upper Limit* |
|---|---|---|---|---|---|---|---|---|---|---|---|---|
| 200 | 1.3% | 6.9% | | | | | | | | | | |
| 300 | 1.1 | 7.5 | | | | | | | | | | |
| 400 | 0.9 | 7.8 | 1.7% | 5.4% | | | | | | | | |
| 500 | 0.9 | 8.0 | 1.5 | 5.7 | | | | | | | | |
| 1,000 | 0.7 | 8.3 | 1.3 | 6.1 | 1.8% | 5.1% | 2.1% | 4.3% | | | | |
| 1,500 | 0.7 | 8.3 | 1.2 | 6.2 | 1.7 | 5.2 | 2.0 | 4.5 | | | | |
| 2,000 | 0.7 | 8.4 | 1.2 | 6.2 | 1.6 | 5.3 | 2.0 | 4.6 | 2.4% | 3.8% | | |
| 2,500 | 0.7 | 8.4 | 1.2 | 6.3 | 1.6 | 5.4 | 1.9 | 4.6 | 2.3 | 3.9 | | |
| 3,000 | 0.7 | 8.4 | 1.2 | 6.3 | 1.6 | 5.4 | 1.9 | 4.7 | 2.3 | 4.0 | | |
| 3,500 | 0.7 | 8.5 | 1.2 | 6.3 | 1.6 | 5.4 | 1.9 | 4.7 | 2.3 | 4.0 | | |
| 4,000 | 0.7 | 8.5 | 1.2 | 6.3 | 1.6 | 5.4 | 1.9 | 4.7 | 2.2 | 4.0 | 2.5% | 3.6% |
| 4,500 | 0.7 | 8.5 | 1.2 | 6.3 | 1.6 | 5.4 | 1.9 | 4.7 | 2.2 | 4.1 | 2.5 | 3.6 |
| 5,000 | 0.6 | 8.5 | 1.2 | 6.4 | 1.6 | 5.4 | 1.9 | 4.7 | 2.2 | 4.1 | 2.5 | 3.6 |
| 6,000 | 0.6 | 8.5 | 1.1 | 6.4 | 1.6 | 5.4 | 1.8 | 4.7 | 2.2 | 4.1 | 2.5 | 3.7 |
| 7,000 | 0.6 | 8.5 | 1.1 | 6.4 | 1.6 | 5.5 | 1.8 | 4.7 | 2.2 | 4.1 | 2.5 | 3.7 |
| 8,000 | 0.6 | 8.5 | 1.1 | 6.4 | 1.6 | 5.5 | 1.8 | 4.8 | 2.2 | 4.1 | 2.4 | 3.7 |
| 9,000 | 0.6 | 8.5 | 1.1 | 6.4 | 1.5 | 5.5 | 1.8 | 4.8 | 2.2 | 4.1 | 2.4 | 3.7 |
| 10,000 | 0.6 | 8.5 | 1.1 | 6.4 | 1.5 | 5.5 | 1.8 | 4.8 | 2.2 | 4.1 | 2.4 | 3.7 |
| 15,000 | 0.6 | 8.5 | 1.1 | 6.4 | 1.5 | 5.5 | 1.8 | 4.8 | 2.1 | 4.2 | 2.4 | 3.7 |
| 20,000 | 0.6 | 8.5 | 1.1 | 6.4 | 1.5 | 5.5 | 1.8 | 4.8 | 2.1 | 4.2 | 2.4 | 3.8 |
| 25,000 | 0.6 | 8.5 | 1.1 | 6.4 | 1.5 | 5.5 | 1.8 | 4.8 | 2.1 | 4.2 | 2.4 | 3.8 |
| 50,000 | 0.6 | 8.5 | 1.1 | 6.4 | 1.5 | 5.5 | 1.8 | 4.8 | 2.1 | 4.2 | 2.4 | 3.8 |
| 100,000 | 0.6 | 8.5 | 1.1 | 6.4 | 1.5 | 5.5 | 1.8 | 4.8 | 2.1 | 4.2 | 2.4 | 3.8 |

## SAMPLE RELIABILITY FOR RELATIVE FREQUENCIES
## FOR RANDOM SAMPLES ONLY

*Rate of Occurrence in Sample 4%*
*Confidence Level 95%*

*For Sample Size of:*

| And Field Size is: | 50 Lower Limit | 50 Upper Limit | 100 Lower Limit | 100 Upper Limit | 200 Lower Limit | 200 Upper Limit | 300 Lower Limit | 300 Upper Limit | 500 Lower Limit | 500 Upper Limit | 1000 Lower Limit | 1000 Upper Limit | 2000 Lower Limit | 2000 Upper Limit |
|---|---|---|---|---|---|---|---|---|---|---|---|---|---|---|
| 200 | 1.0% | 12.4% | 2.0% | 8.2% | | | | | | | | | | |
| 300 | 0.8 | 12.9 | 1.6 | 8.8 | | | | | | | | | | |
| 400 | 0.7 | 13.1 | 1.5 | 9.1 | 2.4% | 6.6% | | | | | | | | |
| 500 | 0.7 | 13.2 | 1.4 | 9.3 | 2.3 | 6.9 | | | | | | | | |
| 1,000 | 0.6 | 13.5 | 1.3 | 9.6 | 2.0 | 7.3 | 2.5% | 6.4% | 3.0% | 5.5% | | | | |
| 1,500 | 0.6 | 13.6 | 1.2 | 9.7 | 1.9 | 7.5 | 2.4 | 6.5 | 2.8 | 5.7 | | | | |
| 2,000 | 0.5 | 13.6 | 1.2 | 9.8 | 1.9 | 7.5 | 2.3 | 6.6 | 2.7 | 5.8 | 3.2% | 5.0% | | |
| 2,500 | 0.5 | 13.6 | 1.2 | 9.8 | 1.8 | 7.6 | 2.3 | 6.6 | 2.7 | 5.8 | 3.2 | 5.1 | | |
| 3,000 | 0.5 | 13.6 | 1.2 | 9.8 | 1.8 | 7.6 | 2.3 | 6.7 | 2.7 | 5.9 | 3.1 | 5.1 | | |
| 3,500 | 0.5 | 13.7 | 1.1 | 9.8 | 1.8 | 7.6 | 2.3 | 6.7 | 2.6 | 5.9 | 3.1 | 5.2 | | |
| 4,000 | 0.5 | 13.7 | 1.1 | 9.9 | 1.8 | 7.6 | 2.2 | 6.7 | 2.6 | 5.9 | 3.1 | 5.2 | 3.5% | 4.7% |
| 4,500 | 0.5 | 13.7 | 1.1 | 9.9 | 1.8 | 7.7 | 2.2 | 6.7 | 2.6 | 5.9 | 3.1 | 5.2 | 3.4 | 4.7 |
| 5,000 | 0.5 | 13.7 | 1.1 | 9.9 | 1.8 | 7.7 | 2.2 | 6.7 | 2.6 | 5.9 | 3.0 | 5.2 | 3.4 | 4.7 |
| 6,000 | 0.5 | 13.7 | 1.1 | 9.9 | 1.8 | 7.7 | 2.2 | 6.7 | 2.6 | 6.0 | 3.0 | 5.2 | 3.4 | 4.8 |
| 7,000 | 0.5 | 13.7 | 1.1 | 9.9 | 1.8 | 7.7 | 2.2 | 6.8 | 2.6 | 6.0 | 3.0 | 5.3 | 3.3 | 4.8 |
| 8,000 | 0.5 | 13.7 | 1.1 | 9.9 | 1.8 | 7.7 | 2.2 | 6.8 | 2.6 | 6.0 | 3.0 | 5.3 | 3.3 | 4.8 |
| 9,000 | 0.5 | 13.7 | 1.1 | 9.9 | 1.8 | 7.7 | 2.2 | 6.8 | 2.6 | 6.0 | 3.0 | 5.3 | 3.3 | 4.8 |
| 10,000 | 0.5 | 13.7 | 1.1 | 9.9 | 1.8 | 7.7 | 2.2 | 6.8 | 2.6 | 6.0 | 3.0 | 5.3 | 3.3 | 4.8 |
| 15,000 | 0.5 | 13.7 | 1.1 | 9.9 | 1.8 | 7.7 | 2.2 | 6.8 | 2.6 | 6.0 | 3.0 | 5.3 | 3.3 | 4.9 |
| 20,000 | 0.5 | 13.7 | 1.1 | 9.9 | 1.8 | 7.7 | 2.2 | 6.8 | 2.6 | 6.0 | 3.0 | 5.3 | 3.3 | 4.9 |
| 25,000 | 0.5 | 13.7 | 1.1 | 9.9 | 1.8 | 7.7 | 2.2 | 6.8 | 2.5 | 6.0 | 2.9 | 5.3 | 3.3 | 4.9 |
| 50,000 | 0.5 | 13.7 | 1.1 | 9.9 | 1.7 | 7.7 | 2.2 | 6.8 | 2.5 | 6.0 | 2.9 | 5.4 | 3.2 | 4.9 |
| 100,000 | 0.5 | 13.7 | 1.1 | 9.9 | 1.7 | 7.7 | 2.2 | 6.8 | 2.5 | 6.0 | 2.9 | 5.4 | 3.2 | 4.9 |

**SAMPLE RELIABILITY FOR RELATIVE FREQUENCIES**

**FOR RANDOM SAMPLES ONLY**

*Rate of Occurrence in Sample 5%*
*Confidence Level 95%*

*For Sample Size of:*

| *And Field Size is:* | 60 *Lower Limit* | 60 *Upper Limit* | 100 *Lower Limit* | 100 *Upper Limit* | 200 *Lower Limit* | 200 *Upper Limit* | 300 *Lower Limit* | 300 *Upper Limit* | 500 *Lower Limit* | 500 *Upper Limit* | 1000 *Lower Limit* | 1000 *Upper Limit* | 2000 *Lower Limit* | 2000 *Upper Limit* |
|---|---|---|---|---|---|---|---|---|---|---|---|---|---|---|
| 200 | 1.7% | 12.5% | 2.6% | 9.5% | | | | | | | | | | |
| 300 | 1.5 | 13.0 | 2.3 | 10.1 | | | | | | | | | | |
| 400 | 1.4 | 13.2 | 2.1 | 10.5 | 3.2% | 7.8% | | | | | | | | |
| 500 | 1.3 | 13.4 | 2.0 | 10.6 | 3.0 | 8.1 | | | | | | | | |
| 1,000 | 1.2 | 13.7 | 1.8 | 11.0 | 2.7 | 8.6 | 3.2% | 7.6% | 3.8% | 6.6% | | | | |
| 1,500 | 1.1 | 13.8 | 1.8 | 11.1 | 2.6 | 8.7 | 3.1 | 7.8 | 3.6 | 6.9 | | | | |
| 2,000 | 1.1 | 13.8 | 1.7 | 11.1 | 2.6 | 8.8 | 3.0 | 7.9 | 3.5 | 7.0 | 4.1% | 6.1% | | |
| 2,500 | 1.1 | 13.8 | 1.7 | 11.2 | 2.5 | 8.8 | 3.0 | 7.9 | 3.5 | 7.1 | 4.0 | 6.2 | | |
| 3,000 | 1.1 | 13.9 | 1.7 | 11.2 | 2.5 | 8.9 | 2.9 | 8.0 | 3.4 | 7.1 | 4.0 | 6.3 | | |
| 3,500 | 1.1 | 13.9 | 1.7 | 11.2 | 2.5 | 8.9 | 2.9 | 8.0 | 3.4 | 7.1 | 3.9 | 6.3 | | |
| 4,000 | 1.1 | 13.9 | 1.7 | 11.2 | 2.5 | 8.9 | 2.9 | 8.0 | 3.4 | 7.1 | 3.9 | 6.3 | 4.4% | 5.7% |
| 4,500 | 1.1 | 13.9 | 1.7 | 11.2 | 2.5 | 8.9 | 2.9 | 8.0 | 3.4 | 7.2 | 3.9 | 6.4 | 4.3 | 5.8 |
| 5,000 | 1.1 | 13.9 | 1.7 | 11.2 | 2.5 | 8.9 | 2.9 | 8.0 | 3.4 | 7.2 | 3.9 | 6.4 | 4.3 | 5.8 |
| 6,000 | 1.1 | 13.9 | 1.7 | 11.2 | 2.5 | 8.9 | 2.9 | 8.0 | 3.3 | 7.2 | 3.8 | 6.4 | 4.3 | 5.9 |
| 7,000 | 1.1 | 13.9 | 1.7 | 11.2 | 2.5 | 8.9 | 2.9 | 8.0 | 3.3 | 7.2 | 3.8 | 6.4 | 4.2 | 5.9 |
| 8,000 | 1.1 | 13.9 | 1.7 | 11.3 | 2.5 | 9.0 | 2.9 | 8.1 | 3.3 | 7.2 | 3.8 | 6.5 | 4.2 | 5.9 |
| 9,000 | 1.1 | 13.9 | 1.7 | 11.3 | 2.5 | 9.0 | 2.9 | 8.1 | 3.3 | 7.2 | 3.8 | 6.5 | 4.2 | 5.9 |
| 10,000 | 1.1 | 13.9 | 1.7 | 11.3 | 2.5 | 9.0 | 2.9 | 8.1 | 3.3 | 7.2 | 3.8 | 6.5 | 4.2 | 5.9 |
| 15,000 | 1.1 | 13.9 | 1.7 | 11.3 | 2.4 | 9.0 | 2.9 | 8.1 | 3.3 | 7.3 | 3.8 | 6.5 | 4.2 | 6.0 |
| 20,000 | 1.1 | 13.9 | 1.7 | 11.3 | 2.4 | 9.0 | 2.8 | 8.1 | 3.3 | 7.3 | 3.8 | 6.5 | 4.1 | 6.0 |
| 25,000 | 1.0 | 13.9 | 1.7 | 11.3 | 2.4 | 9.0 | 2.8 | 8.1 | 3.3 | 7.3 | 3.8 | 6.5 | 4.1 | 6.0 |
| 50,000 | 1.0 | 13.9 | 1.6 | 11.3 | 2.4 | 9.0 | 2.8 | 8.1 | 3.3 | 7.3 | 3.8 | 6.5 | 4.1 | 6.0 |
| 100,000 | 1.0 | 13.9 | 1.6 | 11.3 | 2.4 | 9.0 | 2.8 | 8.1 | 3.3 | 7.3 | 3.7 | 6.5 | 4.1 | 6.0 |

**SAMPLE RELIABILITY FOR RELATIVE FREQUENCIES**

**FOR RANDOM SAMPLES ONLY**

*Rate of Occurrence in Sample 6%*
*Confidence Level 95%*

*For Sample Size of:*

| *And Field Size is:* | 50 | | 100 | | 200 | | 300 | | 500 | | 1000 | | 2000 | |
|---|---|---|---|---|---|---|---|---|---|---|---|---|---|---|
| | *Lower Limit* | *Upper Limit* | *Lower Limit* | *Upper Limit* | *Lower Limit* | *Upper Limit* | *Lower Limit* | *Upper Limit* | *Lower Limit* | *Upper Limit* | *Lower Limit* | *Upper Limit* | *Lower Limit* | *Upper Limit* |
| 200 | 1.9% | 15.2% | 3.3% | 10.7% | | | | | | | | | | |
| 300 | 1.7 | 15.7 | 2.9 | 11.4 | | | | | | | | | | |
| 400 | 1.6 | 15.9 | 2.7 | 11.7 | 4.0% | 9.0% | | | | | | | | |
| 500 | 1.5 | 16.0 | 2.6 | 11.9 | 3.8 | 9.3 | | | | | | | | |
| 1,000 | 1.4 | 16.3 | 2.4 | 12.3 | 3.5 | 9.8 | 4.0% | 8.7% | 4.7% | 7.7% | | | | |
| 1,500 | 1.3 | 16.4 | 2.4 | 12.4 | 3.4 | 9.9 | 3.9 | 8.9 | 4.5 | 8.0 | | | | |
| 2,000 | 1.3 | 16.4 | 2.3 | 12.4 | 3.3 | 10.0 | 3.8 | 9.0 | 4.4 | 8.1 | 5.0% | 7.2% | | |
| 2,500 | 1.3 | 16.5 | 2.3 | 12.5 | 3.3 | 10.0 | 3.8 | 9.1 | 4.3 | 8.2 | 4.9 | 7.3 | | |
| 3,000 | 1.3 | 16.5 | 2.3 | 12.5 | 3.3 | 10.1 | 3.8 | 9.1 | 4.3 | 8.2 | 4.9 | 7.3 | | |
| 3,500 | 1.3 | 16.5 | 2.3 | 12.5 | 3.3 | 10.1 | 3.7 | 9.1 | 4.3 | 8.3 | 4.8 | 7.4 | | |
| 4,000 | 1.3 | 16.5 | 2.3 | 12.5 | 3.3 | 10.1 | 3.7 | 9.2 | 4.2 | 8.3 | 4.8 | 7.4 | 5.3% | 6.8% |
| 4,500 | 1.3 | 16.5 | 2.3 | 12.5 | 3.2 | 10.1 | 3.7 | 9.2 | 4.2 | 8.3 | 4.8 | 7.5 | 5.3 | 6.8 |
| 5,000 | 1.3 | 16.5 | 2.3 | 12.5 | 3.2 | 10.1 | 3.7 | 9.2 | 4.2 | 8.3 | 4.8 | 7.5 | 5.2 | 6.9 |
| 6,000 | 1.3 | 16.5 | 2.3 | 12.5 | 3.2 | 10.1 | 3.7 | 9.2 | 4.2 | 8.3 | 4.8 | 7.5 | 5.2 | 6.9 |
| 7,000 | 1.3 | 16.5 | 2.3 | 12.6 | 3.2 | 10.2 | 3.7 | 9.2 | 4.2 | 8.3 | 4.7 | 7.5 | 5.2 | 7.0 |
| 8,000 | 1.3 | 16.5 | 2.3 | 12.6 | 3.2 | 10.2 | 3.7 | 9.2 | 4.2 | 8.4 | 4.7 | 7.5 | 5.1 | 7.0 |
| 9,000 | 1.3 | 16.5 | 2.3 | 12.6 | 3.2 | 10.2 | 3.7 | 9.2 | 4.2 | 8.4 | 4.7 | 7.6 | 5.1 | 7.0 |
| 10,000 | 1.3 | 16.5 | 2.3 | 12.6 | 3.2 | 10.2 | 3.7 | 9.2 | 4.2 | 8.4 | 4.7 | 7.6 | 5.1 | 7.0 |
| 15,000 | 1.3 | 16.6 | 2.3 | 12.6 | 3.2 | 10.2 | 3.7 | 9.3 | 4.1 | 8.4 | 4.7 | 7.6 | 5.1 | 7.0 |
| 20,000 | 1.3 | 16.6 | 2.3 | 12.6 | 3.2 | 10.2 | 3.7 | 9.3 | 4.1 | 8.4 | 4.6 | 7.6 | 5.1 | 7.1 |
| 25,000 | 1.3 | 16.6 | 2.3 | 12.6 | 3.2 | 10.2 | 3.6 | 9.3 | 4.1 | 8.4 | 4.6 | 7.6 | 5.1 | 7.1 |
| 50,000 | 1.3 | 16.6 | 2.2 | 12.6 | 3.2 | 10.2 | 3.6 | 9.3 | 4.1 | 8.4 | 4.6 | 7.6 | 5.0 | 7.1 |
| 100,000 | 1.3 | 16.6 | 2.2 | 12.6 | 3.2 | 10.2 | 3.6 | 9.3 | 4.1 | 8.4 | 4.6 | 7.6 | 5.0 | 7.1 |

**SAMPLE RELIABILITY FOR RELATIVE FREQUENCIES**

**FOR RANDOM SAMPLES ONLY**

*Rate of Occurrence in Sample 7%*
*Confidence Level 95%*

*For Sample Size of:*

| *And* | 100 | | 200 | | 300 | | 500 | | 1000 | | 2000 | |
|---|---|---|---|---|---|---|---|---|---|---|---|---|
| *Field Size is:* | *Lower Limit* | *Upper Limit* | *Lower Limit* | *Upper Limit* | *Lower Limit* | *Upper Limit* | *Lower Limit* | *Upper Limit* | *Lower Limit* | *Upper Limit* | *Lower Limit* | *Upper Limit* |
| 200 | 4.1% | 11.9% | | | | | | | | | | |
| 300 | 3.6 | 12.6 | | | | | | | | | | |
| 400 | 3.4 | 13.0 | 4.8% | 10.1% | | | | | | | | |
| 500 | 3.3 | 13.2 | 4.6 | 10.4 | | | | | | | | |
| 1,000 | 3.1 | 13.6 | 4.3 | 10.9 | 4.9% | 9.9% | 5.6% | 8.8% | | | | |
| 1,500 | 3.0 | 13.7 | 4.2 | 11.1 | 4.7 | 10.1 | 5.3 | 9.1 | | | | |
| 2,000 | 3.0 | 13.7 | 4.1 | 11.2 | 4.6 | 10.2 | 5.2 | 9.2 | 6.0% | 8.2% | | |
| 2,500 | 2.9 | 13.8 | 4.1 | 11.2 | 4.6 | 10.2 | 5.2 | 9.3 | 5.9 | 8.3 | | |
| 3,000 | 2.9 | 13.8 | 4.0 | 11.3 | 4.6 | 10.3 | 5.1 | 9.3 | 5.8 | 8.4 | | |
| 3,500 | 2.9 | 13.8 | 4.0 | 11.3 | 4.6 | 10.3 | 5.1 | 9.4 | 5.8 | 8.5 | | |
| 4,000 | 2.9 | 13.8 | 4.0 | 11.3 | 4.5 | 10.3 | 5.1 | 9.4 | 5.7 | 8.5 | 6.3% | 7.8% |
| 4,500 | 2.9 | 13.8 | 4.0 | 11.3 | 4.5 | 10.3 | 5.1 | 9.4 | 5.7 | 8.5 | 6.2 | 7.9 |
| 5,000 | 2.9 | 13.8 | 4.0 | 11.3 | 4.5 | 10.3 | 5.1 | 9.4 | 5.7 | 8.6 | 6.2 | 7.9 |
| 6,000 | 2.9 | 13.8 | 4.0 | 11.3 | 4.5 | 10.4 | 5.1 | 9.5 | 5.7 | 8.6 | 6.1 | 8.0 |
| 7,000 | 2.9 | 13.9 | 4.0 | 11.4 | 4.5 | 10.4 | 5.0 | 9.5 | 5.6 | 8.6 | 6.1 | 8.0 |
| 8,000 | 2.9 | 13.9 | 4.0 | 11.4 | 4.5 | 10.4 | 5.0 | 9.5 | 5.6 | 8.6 | 6.1 | 8.0 |
| 9,000 | 2.9 | 13.9 | 4.0 | 11.4 | 4.5 | 10.4 | 5.0 | 9.5 | 5.6 | 8.6 | 6.1 | 8.1 |
| 10,000 | 2.9 | 13.9 | 4.0 | 11.4 | 4.5 | 10.4 | 5.0 | 9.5 | 5.6 | 8.6 | 6.1 | 8.1 |
| 15,000 | 2.9 | 13.9 | 4.0 | 11.4 | 4.5 | 10.4 | 5.0 | 9.5 | 5.6 | 8.7 | 6.0 | 8.1 |
| 20,000 | 2.9 | 13.9 | 4.0 | 11.4 | 4.5 | 10.4 | 5.0 | 9.5 | 5.6 | 8.7 | 6.0 | 8.1 |
| 25,000 | 2.9 | 13.9 | 4.0 | 11.4 | 4.5 | 10.4 | 5.0 | 9.5 | 5.6 | 8.7 | 6.0 | 8.1 |
| 50,000 | 2.9 | 13.9 | 4.0 | 11.4 | 4.5 | 10.4 | 5.0 | 9.6 | 5.5 | 8.7 | 6.0 | 8.2 |
| 100,000 | 2.9 | 13.9 | 3.9 | 11.4 | 4.4 | 10.4 | 5.0 | 9.6 | 5.5 | 8.7 | 6.0 | 8.2 |

**SAMPLE RELIABILITY FOR RELATIVE FREQUENCIES**

**FOR RANDOM SAMPLES ONLY**

*Rate of Occurrence in Sample 8%*
*Confidence Level 95%*

*For Sample Size of:*

| *And Field Size is:* | 50 *Lower Limit* | 50 *Upper Limit* | 100 *Lower Limit* | 100 *Upper Limit* | 200 *Lower Limit* | 200 *Upper Limit* | 300 *Lower Limit* | 300 *Upper Limit* | 500 *Lower Limit* | 500 *Upper Limit* | 1000 *Lower Limit* | 1000 *Upper Limit* | 2000 *Lower Limit* | 2000 *Upper Limit* |
|---|---|---|---|---|---|---|---|---|---|---|---|---|---|---|
| 200 | 3.0% | 17.7% | 4.8% | 13.1% | | | | | | | | | | |
| 300 | 2.7 | 18.3 | 4.3 | 13.9 | | | | | | | | | | |
| 400 | 2.6 | 18.5 | 4.1 | 14.2 | 5.7% | 11.3% | | | | | | | | |
| 500 | 2.5 | 18.7 | 4.0 | 14.4 | 5.4 | 11.6 | | | | | | | | |
| 1,000 | 2.4 | 19.0 | 3.7 | 14.8 | 5.1 | 12.1 | 5.7% | 11.0% | 6.5% | 9.9% | | | | |
| 1,500 | 2.3 | 19.1 | 3.7 | 14.9 | 4.9 | 12.3 | 5.5 | 11.2 | 6.2 | 10.2 | | | | |
| 2,000 | 2.3 | 19.1 | 3.6 | 15.0 | 4.9 | 12.4 | 5.5 | 11.3 | 6.1 | 10.3 | 6.9% | 9.3% | | |
| 2,500 | 2.3 | 19.1 | 3.6 | 15.0 | 4.8 | 12.4 | 5.4 | 11.4 | 6.0 | 10.4 | 6.8 | 9.4 | | |
| 3,000 | 2.3 | 19.2 | 3.6 | 15.0 | 4.8 | 12.5 | 5.4 | 11.4 | 6.0 | 10.5 | 6.7 | 9.5 | | |
| 3,500 | 2.3 | 19.2 | 3.6 | 15.1 | 4.8 | 12.5 | 5.4 | 11.5 | 6.0 | 10.5 | 6.7 | 9.6 | | |
| 4,000 | 2.3 | 19.2 | 3.6 | 15.1 | 4.8 | 12.5 | 5.4 | 11.5 | 6.0 | 10.5 | 6.6 | 9.6 | 7.2% | 8.9% |
| 4,500 | 2.3 | 19.2 | 3.6 | 15.1 | 4.8 | 12.5 | 5.3 | 11.5 | 5.9 | 10.6 | 6.6 | 9.6 | 7.2 | 8.9 |
| 5,000 | 2.3 | 19.2 | 3.6 | 15.1 | 4.8 | 12.5 | 5.3 | 11.5 | 5.9 | 10.6 | 6.6 | 9.6 | 7.1 | 9.9 |
| 6,000 | 2.3 | 19.2 | 3.6 | 15.1 | 4.8 | 12.5 | 5.3 | 11.5 | 5.9 | 10.6 | 6.6 | 9.7 | 7.1 | 9.0 |
| 7,000 | 2.3 | 19.2 | 3.5 | 15.1 | 4.8 | 12.5 | 5.3 | 11.5 | 5.9 | 10.6 | 6.5 | 9.7 | 7.0 | 9.1 |
| 8,000 | 2.3 | 19.2 | 3.5 | 15.1 | 4.7 | 12.6 | 5.3 | 11.6 | 5.9 | 10.6 | 6.5 | 9.7 | 7.0 | 9.1 |
| 9,000 | 2.3 | 19.2 | 3.5 | 15.1 | 4.7 | 12.6 | 5.3 | 11.6 | 5.9 | 10.6 | 6.5 | 9.7 | 7.0 | 9.1 |
| 10,000 | 2.2 | 19.2 | 3.5 | 15.1 | 4.7 | 12.6 | 5.3 | 11.6 | 5.9 | 10.6 | 6.5 | 9.7 | 7.0 | 9.1 |
| 15,000 | 2.2 | 19.2 | 3.5 | 15.1 | 4.7 | 12.6 | 5.3 | 11.6 | 5.9 | 10.7 | 6.5 | 9.8 | 7.0 | 9.2 |
| 20,000 | 2.2 | 19.2 | 3.5 | 15.1 | 4.7 | 12.6 | 5.3 | 11.6 | 5.8 | 10.7 | 6.5 | 9.8 | 6.9 | 9.2 |
| 25,000 | 2.2 | 19.2 | 3.5 | 15.2 | 4.7 | 12.6 | 5.3 | 11.6 | 5.8 | 10.7 | 6.5 | 9.8 | 6.9 | 9.2 |
| 50,000 | 2.2 | 19.2 | 3.5 | 15.2 | 4.7 | 12.6 | 5.3 | 11.6 | 5.8 | 10.7 | 6.4 | 9.8 | 6.9 | 9.2 |
| 100,000 | 2.2 | 19.3 | 3.5 | 15.2 | 4.7 | 12.6 | 5.2 | 11.6 | 5.8 | 10.7 | 6.4 | 9.8 | 6.9 | 9.3 |

TABLE 6 (Continued)

**SAMPLE RELIABILITY FOR RELATIVE FREQUENCIES**

**FOR RANDOM SAMPLES ONLY**

*Rate of Occurrence in Sample 9%*
*Confidence Level 95%*

*For Sample Size of:*

| *And Field Size is:* | *100* | | *200* | | *300* | | *500* | | *1000* | | *2000* | |
|---|---|---|---|---|---|---|---|---|---|---|---|---|
| | *Lower Limit* | *Upper Limit* | *Lower Limit* | *Upper Limit* | *Lower Limit* | *Upper Limit* | *Lower Limit* | *Upper Limit* | *Lower Limit* | *Upper Limit* | *Lower Limit* | *Upper Limit* |
| 200 | 5.6% | 14.2% | | | | | | | | | | |
| 300 | 5.1 | 15.0 | | | | | | | | | | |
| 400 | 4.8 | 15.4 | 6.5% | 12.4% | | | | | | | | |
| 500 | 4.7 | 15.6 | 6.3 | 12.7 | | | | | | | | |
| 1,000 | 4.5 | 16.0 | 5.8 | 13.3 | 6.5% | 12.2% | 7.4% | 11.0% | | | | |
| 1,500 | 4.4 | 16.2 | 5.7 | 13.5 | 6.4 | 12.4 | 7.1 | 11.3 | | | | |
| 2,000 | 4.3 | 16.2 | 5.6 | 13.6 | 6.3 | 12.5 | 7.0 | 11.5 | 7.8% | 10.4% | | |
| 2,500 | 4.3 | 16.3 | 5.6 | 13.6 | 6.2 | 12.6 | 6.9 | 11.5 | 7.7 | 10.5 | | |
| 3,000 | 4.3 | 16.3 | 5.6 | 13.7 | 6.2 | 12.6 | 6.9 | 11.6 | 7.6 | 10.6 | | |
| 3,500 | 4.3 | 16.3 | 5.6 | 13.7 | 6.2 | 12.6 | 6.8 | 11.6 | 7.6 | 10.6 | | |
| 4,000 | 4.3 | 16.3 | 5.6 | 13.7 | 6.2 | 12.7 | 6.8 | 11.7 | 7.5 | 10.7 | 8.1% | 9.9% |
| 4,500 | 4.3 | 16.3 | 5.5 | 13.7 | 6.2 | 12.7 | 6.8 | 11.7 | 7.5 | 10.7 | 8.1 | 10.0 |
| 5,000 | 4.3 | 16.3 | 5.5 | 13.7 | 6.1 | 12.7 | 6.8 | 11.7 | 7.5 | 10.7 | 8.1 | 10.0 |
| 6,000 | 4.2 | 16.3 | 5.5 | 13.7 | 6.1 | 12.7 | 6.8 | 11.7 | 7.5 | 10.8 | 8.0 | 10.1 |
| 7,000 | 4.2 | 16.4 | 5.5 | 13.8 | 6.1 | 12.7 | 6.8 | 11.7 | 7.4 | 10.8 | 8.0 | 10.1 |
| 8,000 | 4.2 | 16.4 | 5.5 | 13.8 | 6.1 | 12.7 | 6.7 | 11.7 | 7.4 | 10.8 | 8.0 | 10.2 |
| 9,000 | 4.2 | 16.4 | 5.5 | 13.8 | 6.1 | 12.7 | 6.7 | 11.8 | 7.4 | 10.8 | 7.9 | 10.2 |
| 10,000 | 4.2 | 16.4 | 5.5 | 13.8 | 6.1 | 12.7 | 6.7 | 11.8 | 7.4 | 10.8 | 7.9 | 10.2 |
| 15,000 | 4.2 | 16.4 | 5.5 | 13.8 | 6.1 | 12.8 | 6.7 | 11.8 | 7.4 | 10.9 | 7.9 | 10.2 |
| 20,000 | 4.2 | 16.4 | 5.5 | 13.8 | 6.1 | 12.8 | 6.7 | 11.8 | 7.4 | 10.9 | 7.9 | 10.3 |
| 25,000 | 4.2 | 16.4 | 5.5 | 13.8 | 6.1 | 12.8 | 6.7 | 11.8 | 7.4 | 10.9 | 7.8 | 10.3 |
| 50,000 | 4.2 | 16.4 | 5.5 | 13.8 | 6.1 | 12.8 | 6.7 | 11.8 | 7.3 | 10.9 | 7.8 | 10.3 |
| 100,000 | 4.2 | 16.4 | 5.5 | 13.8 | 6.1 | 12.8 | 6.7 | 11.8 | 7.3 | 10.9 | 7.8 | 10.3 |

## SAMPLE RELIABILITY FOR RELATIVE FREQUENCIES
## FOR RANDOM SAMPLES ONLY

*Rate of Occurrence in Sample 10%*
*Confidence Level 95%*

*For Sample Size of:*

| *And Field Size is:* | 50 *Lower Limit* | 50 *Upper Limit* | 100 *Lower Limit* | 100 *Upper Limit* | 200 *Lower Limit* | 200 *Upper Limit* | 300 *Lower Limit* | 300 *Upper Limit* | 500 *Lower Limit* | 500 *Upper Limit* | 1000 *Lower Limit* | 1000 *Upper Limit* | 2000 *Lower Limit* | 2000 *Upper Limit* |
|---|---|---|---|---|---|---|---|---|---|---|---|---|---|---|
| 200 | 4.2% | 20.2% | 6.4% | 15.4% | | | | | | | | | | |
| 300 | 3.9 | 20.8 | 5.8 | 16.2 | | | | | | | | | | |
| 400 | 3.8 | 21.1 | 5.6 | 16.6 | 7.3% | 13.6% | | | | | | | | |
| 500 | 3.7 | 21.2 | 5.4 | 16.8 | 7.1 | 13.9 | | | | | | | | |
| 1,000 | 3.5 | 21.5 | 5.2 | 17.3 | 6.6 | 14.5 | 7.4% | 13.3% | 8.2% | 12.1% | | | | |
| 1,500 | 3.4 | 21.6 | 5.1 | 17.4 | 6.5 | 14.7 | 7.2 | 13.6 | 8.0 | 12.4 | | | | |
| 2,000 | 3.4 | 21.7 | 5.0 | 17.4 | 6.4 | 14.8 | 7.1 | 13.7 | 7.9 | 12.6 | 8.7% | 11.4% | | |
| 2,500 | 3.4 | 21.7 | 5.0 | 17.5 | 6.4 | 14.8 | 7.0 | 13.7 | 7.8 | 12.7 | 8.6 | 11.6 | | |
| 3,000 | 3.4 | 21.7 | 5.0 | 17.5 | 6.4 | 14.9 | 7.0 | 13.8 | 7.7 | 12.7 | 8.5 | 11.7 | | |
| 3,500 | 3.4 | 21.7 | 5.0 | 17.5 | 6.3 | 14.9 | 7.0 | 13.8 | 7.7 | 12.8 | 8.5 | 11.7 | | |
| 4,000 | 3.4 | 21.8 | 5.0 | 17.5 | 6.3 | 14.9 | 7.0 | 13.8 | 7.7 | 12.8 | 8.5 | 11.8 | 9.1% | 11.0% |
| 4,500 | 3.4 | 21.8 | 5.0 | 17.5 | 6.3 | 14.9 | 7.0 | 13.8 | 7.7 | 12.8 | 8.4 | 11.8 | 9.1 | 11.0 |
| 5,000 | 3.4 | 21.8 | 5.0 | 17.5 | 6.3 | 14.9 | 7.0 | 13.9 | 7.6 | 12.8 | 8.4 | 11.8 | 9.0 | 11.1 |
| 6,000 | 3.4 | 21.8 | 5.0 | 17.6 | 6.3 | 14.9 | 6.9 | 13.9 | 7.6 | 12.8 | 8.4 | 11.9 | 9.0 | 11.1 |
| 7,000 | 3.3 | 21.8 | 4.9 | 17.6 | 6.3 | 15.0 | 6.9 | 13.9 | 7.6 | 12.9 | 8.3 | 11.9 | 8.9 | 11.2 |
| 8,000 | 3.3 | 21.8 | 4.9 | 17.6 | 6.3 | 15.0 | 6.9 | 13.9 | 7.6 | 12.9 | 8.3 | 11.9 | 8.9 | 11.2 |
| 9,000 | 3.3 | 21.8 | 4.9 | 17.6 | 6.3 | 15.0 | 6.9 | 13.9 | 7.6 | 12.9 | 8.3 | 11.9 | 8.9 | 11.2 |
| 10,000 | 3.3 | 21.8 | 4.9 | 17.6 | 6.3 | 15.0 | 6.9 | 13.9 | 7.6 | 12.9 | 8.3 | 11.9 | 8.9 | 11.3 |
| 15,000 | 3.3 | 21.8 | 4.9 | 17.6 | 6.2 | 15.0 | 6.9 | 13.9 | 7.6 | 12.9 | 8.3 | 12.0 | 8.8 | 11.3 |
| 20,000 | 3.3 | 21.8 | 4.9 | 17.6 | 6.2 | 15.0 | 6.9 | 13.9 | 7.6 | 12.9 | 8.3 | 12.0 | 8.8 | 11.3 |
| 25,000 | 3.3 | 21.8 | 4.9 | 17.6 | 6.2 | 15.0 | 6.9 | 14.0 | 7.5 | 12.9 | 8.3 | 12.0 | 8.8 | 11.3 |
| 50,000 | 3.3 | 21.8 | 4.9 | 17.6 | 6.2 | 15.0 | 6.9 | 14.0 | 7.5 | 13.0 | 8.2 | 12.0 | 8.7 | 11.4 |
| 100,000 | 3.3 | 21.8 | 4.9 | 17.6 | 6.2 | 15.0 | 6.9 | 14.0 | 7.5 | 13.0 | 8.2 | 12.0 | 8.7 | 11.4 |

**SAMPLE RELIABILITY FOR RELATIVE FREQUENCIES**

**FOR RANDOM SAMPLES ONLY**

*Rate of Occurrence in Sample 11%*
*Confidence Level 95%*

*For Sample Size of:*

| *And Field Size is:* | 100 | | 200 | | 300 | | 500 | | 1000 | | 2000 | |
|---|---|---|---|---|---|---|---|---|---|---|---|---|
| | *Lower Limit* | *Upper Limit* | *Lower Limit* | *Upper Limit* | *Lower Limit* | *Upper Limit* | *Lower Limit* | *Upper Limit* | *Lower Limit* | *Upper Limit* | *Lower Limit* | *Upper Limit* |
| 200 | 7.2% | 16.5% | | | | | | | | | | |
| 300 | 6.6 | 17.4 | | | | | | | | | | |
| 400 | 6.4 | 17.8 | 8.2% | 14.7% | | | | | | | | |
| 500 | 6.2 | 18.0 | 7.9 | 15.0 | | | | | | | | |
| 1,000 | 5.9 | 18.4 | 7.5 | 15.6 | 8.3% | 14.4% | 9.2% | 13.2% | | | | |
| 1,500 | 5.8 | 18.5 | 7.3 | 15.8 | 8.1 | 14.7 | 8.9 | 13.5 | | | | |
| 2,000 | 5.8 | 18.6 | 7.3 | 15.9 | 8.0 | 14.8 | 8.8 | 13.7 | 9.7% | 12.5% | | |
| 2,500 | 5.8 | 18.6 | 7.2 | 16.0 | 7.9 | 14.8 | 8.7 | 13.7 | 9.6 | 12.6 | | |
| 3,000 | 5.7 | 18.7 | 7.2 | 16.0 | 7.9 | 14.9 | 8.6 | 13.8 | 9.5 | 12.7 | | |
| 3,500 | 5.7 | 18.7 | 7.2 | 16.0 | 7.9 | 14.9 | 8.6 | 13.8 | 9.4 | 12.8 | | |
| 4,000 | 5.7 | 18.7 | 7.2 | 16.0 | 7.8 | 14.9 | 8.6 | 13.9 | 9.4 | 12.8 | 10.1% | 12.0% |
| 4,500 | 5.7 | 18.7 | 7.1 | 16.0 | 7.8 | 14.9 | 8.6 | 13.9 | 9.4 | 12.9 | 10.0 | 12.1 |
| 5,000 | 5.7 | 18.7 | 7.1 | 16.1 | 7.8 | 15.0 | 8.5 | 13.9 | 9.3 | 12.9 | 10.0 | 12.1 |
| 6,000 | 5.7 | 18.7 | 7.1 | 16.1 | 7.8 | 15.0 | 8.5 | 13.9 | 9.3 | 12.9 | 9.9 | 12.2 |
| 7,000 | 5.7 | 18.7 | 7.1 | 16.1 | 7.8 | 15.0 | 8.5 | 14.0 | 9.3 | 12.9 | 9.9 | 12.2 |
| 8,000 | 5.7 | 18.8 | 7.1 | 16.1 | 7.8 | 15.0 | 8.5 | 14.0 | 9.3 | 13.0 | 9.9 | 12.3 |
| 9,000 | 5.7 | 18.8 | 7.1 | 16.1 | 7.8 | 15.0 | 8.5 | 14.0 | 9.3 | 13.0 | 9.8 | 12.3 |
| 10,000 | 5.7 | 18.8 | 7.1 | 16.1 | 7.8 | 15.0 | 8.5 | 14.0 | 9.2 | 13.0 | 9.8 | 12.3 |
| 15,000 | 5.7 | 18.8 | 7.1 | 16.1 | 7.7 | 15.0 | 8.5 | 14.0 | 9.2 | 13.0 | 9.8 | 12.4 |
| 20,000 | 5.7 | 18.8 | 7.1 | 16.1 | 7.7 | 15.1 | 8.4 | 14.0 | 9.2 | 13.1 | 9.7 | 12.4 |
| 25,000 | 5.7 | 18.8 | 7.1 | 16.1 | 7.7 | 15.1 | 8.4 | 14.0 | 9.2 | 13.1 | 9.7 | 12.4 |
| 50,000 | 5.7 | 18.8 | 7.1 | 16.2 | 7.7 | 15.1 | 8.4 | 14.0 | 9.2 | 13.1 | 9.7 | 12.4 |
| 100,000 | 5.7 | 18.8 | 7.1 | 16.2 | 7.7 | 15.1 | 8.4 | 14.1 | 9.2 | 13.1 | 9.7 | 12.4 |

TABLE 6 (Continued)

## SAMPLE RELIABILITY FOR RELATIVE FREQUENCIES

## FOR RANDOM SAMPLES ONLY

*Rate of Occurrence in Sample 12%*
*Confidence Level 95%*

| And Field Size is: | *For Sample Size of:* 50 Lower Limit | 50 Upper Limit | 100 Lower Limit | 100 Upper Limit | 200 Lower Limit | 200 Upper Limit | 300 Lower Limit | 300 Upper Limit | 500 Lower Limit | 500 Upper Limit | 1000 Lower Limit | 1000 Upper Limit | 2000 Lower Limit | 2000 Upper Limit |
|---|---|---|---|---|---|---|---|---|---|---|---|---|---|---|
| 200 | 5.5% | 22.7% | 8.0% | 17.6% | | | | | | | | | | |
| 300 | 5.2 | 23.2 | 7.4 | 18.5 | | | | | | | | | | |
| 400 | 5.0 | 23.5 | 7.2 | 18.9 | 9.1% | 15.8% | | | | | | | | |
| 500 | 4.9 | 23.7 | 7.0 | 19.1 | 8.8 | 16.1 | | | | | | | | |
| 1,000 | 4.7 | 24.0 | 6.7 | 19.6 | 8.3 | 16.7 | 9.1% | 15.5% | 10.1% | 14.2% | | | | |
| 1,500 | 4.7 | 24.1 | 6.6 | 19.7 | 8.2 | 16.9 | 8.9 | 15.8 | 9.8 | 14.6 | | | | |
| 2,000 | 4.6 | 24.2 | 6.5 | 19.8 | 8.1 | 17.0 | 8.8 | 15.9 | 9.7 | 14.7 | 10.6% | 13.5% | | |
| 2,500 | 4.6 | 24.2 | 6.5 | 19.8 | 8.0 | 17.1 | 8.8 | 15.9 | 9.6 | 14.8 | 10.5 | 13.7 | | |
| 3,000 | 4.6 | 24.2 | 6.5 | 19.9 | 8.0 | 17.1 | 8.8 | 16.0 | 9.5 | 14.9 | 10.4 | 13.8 | | |
| 3,500 | 4.6 | 24.2 | 6.5 | 19.9 | 8.0 | 17.2 | 8.7 | 16.0 | 9.5 | 14.9 | 10.4 | 13.8 | | |
| 4,000 | 4.6 | 24.2 | 6.5 | 19.9 | 8.0 | 17.2 | 8.7 | 16.0 | 9.5 | 15.0 | 10.3 | 13.9 | 11.0% | 13.1% |
| 4,500 | 4.6 | 24.2 | 6.5 | 19.9 | 8.0 | 17.2 | 8.7 | 16.1 | 9.5 | 15.0 | 10.3 | 13.9 | 11.0 | 13.1 |
| 5,000 | 4.6 | 24.3 | 6.5 | 19.9 | 8.0 | 17.2 | 8.7 | 16.1 | 9.4 | 15.0 | 19.3 | 13.9 | 10.9 | 13.2 |
| 6,000 | 4.6 | 24.3 | 6.5 | 19.9 | 7.9 | 17.2 | 8.7 | 16.1 | 9.4 | 15.0 | 10.2 | 14.0 | 10.9 | 13.2 |
| 7,000 | 4.6 | 24.3 | 6.4 | 19.9 | 7.9 | 17.2 | 8.6 | 16.1 | 9.4 | 15.0 | 10.2 | 14.0 | 10.8 | 13.3 |
| 8,000 | 4.6 | 24.3 | 6.4 | 19.9 | 7.9 | 17.2 | 8.6 | 16.1 | 9.4 | 15.1 | 10.2 | 14.0 | 10.8 | 13.3 |
| 9,000 | 4.6 | 24.3 | 6.4 | 19.9 | 7.9 | 17.2 | 8.6 | 16.1 | 9.4 | 15.1 | 10.2 | 14.0 | 10.8 | 13.3 |
| 10,000 | 4.6 | 24.3 | 6.4 | 19.9 | 7.9 | 17.3 | 8.6 | 16.1 | 9.4 | 15.1 | 10.2 | 14.1 | 10.8 | 13.3 |
| 15,000 | 4.6 | 24.3 | 6.4 | 20.0 | 7.9 | 17.3 | 8.6 | 16.2 | 9.4 | 15.1 | 10.1 | 14.1 | 10.7 | 13.4 |
| 20,000 | 4.6 | 24.3 | 6.4 | 20.0 | 7.9 | 17.3 | 8.6 | 16.2 | 9.3 | 15.1 | 10.1 | 14.1 | 10.7 | 13.4 |
| 25,000 | 4.6 | 24.3 | 6.4 | 20.0 | 7.9 | 17.3 | 8.6 | 16.2 | 9.3 | 15.1 | 10.1 | 14.1 | 10.7 | 13.4 |
| 50,000 | 4.5 | 24.3 | 6.4 | 20.0 | 7.9 | 17.3 | 8.6 | 16.2 | 9.3 | 15.1 | 10.1 | 14.1 | 10.7 | 13.5 |
| 100,000 | 4.5 | 24.3 | 6.4 | 20.0 | 7.9 | 17.3 | 8.6 | 16.2 | 9.3 | 15.2 | 10.1 | 14.2 | 10.6 | 13.5 |

## SAMPLE RELIABILITY FOR RELATIVE FREQUENCIES
## FOR RANDOM SAMPLES ONLY

*Rate of Occurrence in Sample 13%*
*Confidence Level 95%*

*For Sample Size of:*

| *And Field Size is:* | 100 *Lower Limit* | 100 *Upper Limit* | 200 *Lower Limit* | 200 *Upper Limit* | 300 *Lower Limit* | 300 *Upper Limit* | 500 *Lower Limit* | 500 *Upper Limit* | 1000 *Lower Limit* | 1000 *Upper Limit* | 2000 *Lower Limit* | 2000 *Upper Limit* |
|---|---|---|---|---|---|---|---|---|---|---|---|---|
| 200 | 8.9% | 18.8% | | | | | | | | | | |
| 300 | 8.2 | 19.7 | | | | | | | | | | |
| 400 | 7.9 | 20.1 | 10.0% | 16.9% | | | | | | | | |
| 500 | 7.8 | 20.3 | 9.7 | 17.2 | | | | | | | | |
| 1,000 | 7.5 | 20.8 | 9.2 | 17.9 | 10.0% | 16.6% | 11.0% | 15.3% | | | | |
| 1,500 | 7.4 | 20.9 | 9.0 | 18.1 | 9.8 | 16.9 | 10.7 | 15.7 | | | | |
| 2,000 | 7.3 | 21.0 | 8.9 | 18.2 | 9.7 | 17.0 | 10.6 | 15.8 | 11.6% | 14.6% | | |
| 2,500 | 7.3 | 21.0 | 8.9 | 18.2 | 9.7 | 17.1 | 10.5 | 15.9 | 11.4 | 14.7 | | |
| 3,000 | 7.3 | 21.0 | 8.9 | 18.3 | 9.6 | 17.1 | 10.4 | 16.0 | 11.4 | 14.8 | | |
| 3,500 | 7.2 | 21.1 | 8.8 | 18.3 | 9.6 | 17.1 | 10.4 | 16.0 | 11.3 | 14.9 | | |
| 4,000 | 7.2 | 21.1 | 8.8 | 18.3 | 9.6 | 17.2 | 10.4 | 16.0 | 11.3 | 14.9 | 12.0% | 14.1% |
| 4,500 | 7.2 | 21.1 | 8.8 | 18.3 | 9.6 | 17.2 | 10.4 | 16.1 | 11.2 | 15.0 | 11.9 | 14.2 |
| 5,000 | 7.2 | 21.1 | 8.8 | 18.3 | 9.5 | 17.2 | 10.3 | 16.1 | 11.2 | 15.0 | 11.9 | 14.2 |
| 6,000 | 7.2 | 21.1 | 8.8 | 18.4 | 9.5 | 17.2 | 10.3 | 16.1 | 11.2 | 15.0 | 11.8 | 14.3 |
| 7,000 | 7.2 | 21.1 | 8.8 | 18.4 | 9.5 | 17.2 | 10.3 | 16.1 | 11.1 | 15.1 | 11.8 | 14.3 |
| 8,000 | 7.2 | 21.1 | 8.8 | 18.4 | 9.5 | 17.2 | 10.3 | 16.2 | 11.1 | 15.1 | 11.8 | 14.3 |
| 9,000 | 7.2 | 21.1 | 8.8 | 18.4 | 9.5 | 17.3 | 10.3 | 16.2 | 11.1 | 15.1 | 11.7 | 14.4 |
| 10,000 | 7.2 | 21.1 | 8.7 | 18.4 | 9.5 | 17.3 | 10.3 | 16.2 | 11.1 | 15.1 | 11.7 | 14.4 |
| 15,000 | 7.2 | 21.1 | 8.7 | 18.4 | 9.5 | 17.3 | 10.3 | 16.2 | 11.1 | 15.2 | 11.7 | 14.4 |
| 20,000 | 7.2 | 21.2 | 8.7 | 18.4 | 9.5 | 17.3 | 10.2 | 16.2 | 11.0 | 15.2 | 11.6 | 14.5 |
| 25,000 | 7.2 | 21.2 | 8.7 | 18.4 | 9.5 | 17.3 | 10.2 | 16.2 | 11.0 | 15.2 | 11.6 | 14.5 |
| 50,000 | 7.2 | 21.2 | 8.7 | 18.4 | 9.4 | 17.3 | 10.2 | 16.2 | 11.0 | 15.2 | 11.6 | 14.5 |
| 100,000 | 7.2 | 21.2 | 8.7 | 18.4 | 9.4 | 17.3 | 10.2 | 16.2 | 11.0 | 15.2 | 11.6 | 14.5 |

TABLE 6 (Continued)

## SAMPLE RELIABILITY FOR RELATIVE FREQUENCIES

## FOR RANDOM SAMPLES ONLY

*Rate of Occurrence in Sample 14%*
*Confidence Level 95%*

| And Field Size is: | For Sample Size of: 50 Lower Limit | 50 Upper Limit | 100 Lower Limit | 100 Upper Limit | 200 Lower Limit | 200 Upper Limit | 300 Lower Limit | 300 Upper Limit | 500 Lower Limit | 500 Upper Limit | 1000 Lower Limit | 1000 Upper Limit | 2000 Lower Limit | 2000 Upper Limit |
|---|---|---|---|---|---|---|---|---|---|---|---|---|---|---|
| 200 | 6.9% | 25.0% | 9.7% | 19.9% | | | | | | | | | | |
| 300 | 6.5 | 25.6 | 9.0 | 20.8 | | | | | | | | | | |
| 400 | 6.4 | 25.9 | 8.7 | 21.2 | 10.8% | 18.0% | | | | | | | | |
| 500 | 6.3 | 26.1 | 8.5 | 21.5 | 10.5 | 18.3 | | | | | | | | |
| 1,000 | 6.0 | 26.4 | 8.2 | 21.9 | 10.0 | 19.0 | 10.9% | 17.7% | 11.9% | 16.4% | | | | |
| 1,500 | 6.0 | 26.5 | 8.1 | 22.1 | 9.8 | 19.2 | 10.7 | 18.0 | 11.6 | 16.7 | | | | |
| 2,000 | 5.9 | 26.6 | 8.1 | 22.1 | 9.8 | 19.3 | 10.6 | 18.1 | 11.5 | 16.9 | 12.5% | 15.6% | | |
| 2,500 | 5.9 | 26.6 | 8.0 | 22.2 | 9.7 | 19.4 | 10.5 | 18.2 | 11.4 | 17.0 | 12.4 | 15.8 | | |
| 3,000 | 5.9 | 26.6 | 8.0 | 22.2 | 9.7 | 19.4 | 10.5 | 18.2 | 11.3 | 17.1 | 12.3 | 15.9 | | |
| 3,500 | 5.9 | 26.7 | 8.0 | 22.2 | 9.7 | 19.4 | 10.5 | 18.2 | 11.3 | 17.1 | 12.2 | 15.9 | | |
| 4,000 | 5.9 | 26.7 | 8.0 | 22.2 | 9.6 | 19.4 | 10.4 | 18.3 | 11.3 | 17.1 | 12.2 | 16.0 | 13.0% | 15.1% |
| 4,500 | 5.9 | 26.7 | 8.0 | 22.3 | 9.6 | 19.5 | 10.4 | 18.3 | 11.3 | 17.2 | 12.2 | 16.0 | 12.9 | 15.2 |
| 5,000 | 5.9 | 26.7 | 8.0 | 22.3 | 9.6 | 19.5 | 10.4 | 18.3 | 11.2 | 17.2 | 12.1 | 16.1 | 12.9 | 15.2 |
| 6,000 | 5.9 | 26.7 | 8.0 | 22.3 | 9.6 | 19.5 | 10.4 | 18.3 | 11.2 | 17.2 | 12.1 | 16.1 | 12.8 | 15.3 |
| 7,000 | 5.9 | 26.7 | 7.9 | 22.3 | 9.6 | 19.5 | 10.4 | 18.3 | 11.2 | 17.2 | 12.1 | 16.1 | 12.7 | 15.3 |
| 8,000 | 5.9 | 26.7 | 7.9 | 22.3 | 9.6 | 19.5 | 10.4 | 18.4 | 11.2 | 17.2 | 12.1 | 16.2 | 12.7 | 15.4 |
| 9,000 | 5.8 | 26.7 | 7.9 | 22.3 | 9.6 | 19.5 | 10.4 | 18.4 | 11.2 | 17.3 | 12.0 | 16.2 | 12.7 | 15.4 |
| 10,000 | 5.8 | 26.7 | 7.9 | 22.3 | 9.6 | 19.5 | 10.4 | 18.4 | 11.2 | 17.3 | 12.0 | 16.2 | 12.7 | 15.4 |
| 15,000 | 5.8 | 26.7 | 7.9 | 22.3 | 9.6 | 19.5 | 10.3 | 18.4 | 11.1 | 17.3 | 12.0 | 16.2 | 12.6 | 15.5 |
| 20,000 | 5.8 | 26.7 | 7.9 | 22.3 | 9.6 | 19.6 | 10.3 | 18.4 | 11.1 | 17.3 | 12.0 | 16.2 | 12.6 | 15.5 |
| 25,000 | 5.8 | 26.7 | 7.9 | 22.3 | 9.6 | 19.6 | 10.3 | 18.4 | 11.1 | 17.3 | 12.0 | 16.3 | 12.6 | 15.5 |
| 50,000 | 5.8 | 26.7 | 7.9 | 22.3 | 9.5 | 19.6 | 10.3 | 18.4 | 11.1 | 17.3 | 11.9 | 16.3 | 12.5 | 15.6 |
| 100,000 | 5.8 | 26.8 | 7.9 | 22.4 | 9.5 | 19.6 | 10.3 | 18.4 | 11.1 | 17.3 | 11.9 | 16.3 | 12.5 | 15.6 |

TABLE 6 (Continued)

## SAMPLE RELIABILITY FOR RELATIVE FREQUENCIES
## FOR RANDOM SAMPLES ONLY

*Rate of Occurrence in Sample 15%*
*Confidence Level 95%*

| *And Field Size is:* | 60 *Lower Limit* | 60 *Upper Limit* | 100 *Lower Limit* | 100 *Upper Limit* | 200 *Lower Limit* | 200 *Upper Limit* | 300 *Lower Limit* | 300 *Upper Limit* | 500 *Lower Limit* | 500 *Upper Limit* | 1000 *Lower Limit* | 1000 *Upper Limit* | 2000 *Lower Limit* | 2000 *Upper Limit* |
|---|---|---|---|---|---|---|---|---|---|---|---|---|---|---|
| | *For Sample Size of:* | | | | | | | | | | | | | |
| 200 | 8.4% | 24.7% | 10.5% | 21.0% | | | | | | | | | | |
| 300 | 7.9 | 25.4 | 9.8 | 22.0 | | | | | | | | | | |
| 400 | 7.7 | 25.7 | 9.5 | 22.4 | 11.7% | 19.0% | | | | | | | | |
| 500 | 7.6 | 25.9 | 9.3 | 22.6 | 11.4 | 19.4 | | | | | | | | |
| 1,000 | 7.3 | 26.2 | 9.0 | 23.1 | 10.9 | 20.1 | 11.8% | 18.8% | 12.9% | 17.4% | | | | |
| 1,500 | 7.3 | 26.4 | 8.9 | 23.2 | 10.7 | 20.3 | 11.6 | 19.1 | 12.5 | 17.8 | | | | |
| 2,000 | 7.2 | 26.4 | 8.8 | 23.3 | 10.6 | 20.4 | 11.5 | 19.2 | 12.4 | 18.0 | 13.5% | 16.7% | | |
| 2,500 | 7.2 | 26.4 | 8.8 | 23.4 | 10.6 | 20.5 | 11.4 | 19.3 | 12.3 | 18.1 | 13.3 | 16.8 | | |
| 3,000 | 7.2 | 26.5 | 8.8 | 23.4 | 10.5 | 20.5 | 11.4 | 19.3 | 12.2 | 18.1 | 13.2 | 16.9 | | |
| 3,500 | 7.2 | 26.5 | 8.7 | 23.4 | 10.5 | 20.6 | 11.3 | 19.4 | 12.2 | 18.2 | 13.2 | 17.0 | | |
| 4,000 | 7.2 | 26.5 | 8.7 | 23.4 | 10.5 | 20.6 | 11.3 | 19.4 | 12.2 | 18.2 | 13.1 | 17.1 | 13.9% | 16.2% |
| 4,500 | 7.2 | 26.5 | 8.7 | 23.4 | 10.5 | 20.6 | 11.3 | 19.4 | 12.2 | 18.2 | 13.1 | 17.1 | 13.9 | 16.2 |
| 5,000 | 7.2 | 26.5 | 8.7 | 23.4 | 10.5 | 20.6 | 11.3 | 19.4 | 12.1 | 18.3 | 13.1 | 17.1 | 13.8 | 16.3 |
| 6,000 | 7.1 | 26.5 | 8.7 | 23.5 | 10.4 | 20.6 | 11.3 | 19.4 | 12.1 | 18.3 | 13.0 | 17.2 | 13.7 | 16.3 |
| 7,000 | 7.1 | 26.5 | 8.7 | 23.5 | 10.4 | 20.6 | 11.2 | 19.5 | 12.1 | 18.3 | 13.0 | 17.2 | 13.7 | 16.4 |
| 8,000 | 7.1 | 26.5 | 8.7 | 23.5 | 10.4 | 20.7 | 11.2 | 19.5 | 12.1 | 18.3 | 13.0 | 17.2 | 13.7 | 16.4 |
| 9,000 | 7.1 | 26.5 | 8.7 | 23.5 | 10.4 | 20.7 | 11.2 | 19.5 | 12.1 | 18.3 | 13.0 | 17.2 | 13.6 | 16.5 |
| 10,000 | 7.1 | 26.5 | 8.7 | 23.5 | 10.4 | 20.7 | 11.2 | 19.5 | 12.1 | 18.4 | 13.0 | 17.3 | 13.6 | 16.5 |
| 15,000 | 7.1 | 26.6 | 8.7 | 23.5 | 10.4 | 20.7 | 11.2 | 19.5 | 12.0 | 18.4 | 12.9 | 17.3 | 13.6 | 16.5 |
| 20,000 | 7.1 | 26.6 | 8.7 | 23.5 | 10.4 | 20.7 | 11.2 | 19.5 | 12.0 | 18.4 | 12.9 | 17.3 | 13.5 | 16.5 |
| 25,000 | 7.1 | 26.6 | 8.7 | 23.5 | 10.4 | 20.7 | 11.2 | 19.5 | 12.0 | 18.4 | 12.9 | 17.3 | 13.5 | 16.6 |
| 50,000 | 7.1 | 26.6 | 8.7 | 23.5 | 10.4 | 20.7 | 11.2 | 19.5 | 12.0 | 18.4 | 12.9 | 17.4 | 13.5 | 16.6 |
| 100,000 | 7.1 | 26.6 | 8.7 | 23.5 | 10.4 | 20.7 | 11.2 | 19.5 | 12.0 | 18.4 | 12.9 | 17.4 | 13.5 | 16.6 |

TABLE 6a

## SAMPLE RELIABILITY FOR RELATIVE FREQUENCIES

## FOR RANDOM SAMPLES ONLY

*Rate of Occurrence in Sample 1%*
*Confidence Level 99%*

*For Sample Size of:*

| *And* | 100 | | 200 | | 300 | | 500 | | 1000 | | 2000 | |
|---|---|---|---|---|---|---|---|---|---|---|---|---|
| *Field Size is:* | *Lower Limit* | *Upper Limit* | *Lower Limit* | *Upper Limit* | *Lower Limit* | *Upper Limit* | *Lower Limit* | *Upper Limit* | *Lower Limit* | *Upper Limit* | *Lower Limit* | *Upper Limit* |
| 200 | 0.3% | 5.4% | | | | | | | | | | |
| 300 | 0.2 | 6.1 | | | | | | | | | | |
| 400 | 0.1 | 6.4 | 0.3% | 3.5% | | | | | | | | |
| 500 | 0.1 | 6.6 | 0.3 | 3.8 | | | | | | | | |
| 1,000 | 0.1 | 6.9 | 0.2 | 4.2 | 0.3% | 3.2% | 0.5% | 2.3% | | | | |
| 1,500 | 0.0* | 7.0 | 0.1 | 4.3 | 0.2 | 3.3 | 0.4 | 2.5 | | | | |
| 2,000 | 0.0* | 7.1 | 0.1 | 4.4 | 0.2 | 3.4 | 0.3 | 2.6 | 0.6 | 1.8 | | |
| 2,500 | 0.0* | 7.1 | 0.1 | 4.4 | 0.2 | 3.5 | 0.3 | 2.6 | 0.5 | 1.9 | | |
| 3,000 | 0.0* | 7.1 | 0.1 | 4.4 | 0.2 | 3.5 | 0.3 | 2.7 | 0.5 | 1.9 | | |
| 3,500 | 0.0* | 7.1 | 0.1 | 4.5 | 0.2 | 3.5 | 0.3 | 2.7 | 0.5 | 2.0 | | |
| 4,000 | 0.0* | 7.1 | 0.1 | 4.5 | 0.2 | 3.5 | 0.3 | 2.7 | 0.5 | 2.0 | 0.7% | 1.5% |
| 4,500 | 0.0* | 7.1 | 0.1 | 4.5 | 0.1 | 3.5 | 0.3 | 2.7 | 0.5 | 2.0 | 0.6 | 1.5 |
| 5,000 | 0.0* | 7.2 | 0.1 | 4.5 | 0.1 | 3.5 | 0.3 | 2.7 | 0.4 | 2.0 | 0.6 | 1.6 |
| 6,000 | 0.0* | 7.2 | 0.1 | 4.5 | 0.1 | 3.5 | 0.3 | 2.7 | 0.4 | 2.0 | 0.6 | 1.6 |
| 7,000 | 0.0* | 7.2 | 0.1 | 4.5 | 0.1 | 3.6 | 0.3 | 2.7 | 0.4 | 2.0 | 0.6 | 1.6 |
| 8,000 | 0.0* | 7.2 | 0.1 | 4.5 | 0.1 | 3.6 | 0.2 | 2.8 | 0.4 | 2.1 | 0.6 | 1.6 |
| 9,000 | 0.0* | 7.2 | 0.1 | 4.5 | 0.1 | 3.6 | 0.2 | 2.8 | 0.4 | 2.1 | 0.6 | 1.6 |
| 10,000 | 0.0* | 7.2 | 0.1 | 4.5 | 0.1 | 3.6 | 0.2 | 2.8 | 0.4 | 2.1 | 0.6 | 1.7 |
| 15,000 | 0.0* | 7.2 | 0.1 | 4.5 | 0.1 | 3.6 | 0.2 | 2.8 | 0.4 | 2.1 | 0.6 | 1.7 |
| 20,000 | 0.0* | 7.2 | 0.1 | 4.5 | 0.1 | 3.6 | 0.2 | 2.8 | 0.4 | 2.1 | 0.6 | 1.7 |
| 25,000 | 0.0* | 7.2 | 0.1 | 4.5 | 0.1 | 3.6 | 0.2 | 2.8 | 0.4 | 2.1 | 0.5 | 1.7 |
| 50,000 | 0.0* | 7.2 | 0.1 | 4.5 | 0.1 | 3.6 | 0.2 | 2.8 | 0.4 | 2.1 | 0.5 | 1.7 |
| 100,000 | 0.0* | 7.2 | 0.1 | 4.6 | 0.1 | 3.6 | 0.2 | 2.8 | 0.4 | 2.1 | 0.5 | 1.7 |

* Less than 0.05%

## SAMPLE RELIABILITY FOR RELATIVE FREQUENCIES
## FOR RANDOM SAMPLES ONLY

*Rate of Occurrence in Sample 2%*
*Confidence Level 99%*

| *And Field Size is:* | *For Sample Size of:* 50 | | 100 | | 200 | | 300 | | 500 | | 1000 | | 2000 | |
|---|---|---|---|---|---|---|---|---|---|---|---|---|---|---|
| | *Lower Limit* | *Upper Limit* | *Lower Limit* | *Upper Limit* | *Lower Limit* | *Upper Limit* | *Lower Limit* | *Upper Limit* | *Lower Limit* | *Upper Limit* | *Lower Limit* | *Upper Limit* | *Lower Limit* | *Upper Limit* |
| 200 | 0.3% | 12.4% | 0.7% | 6.9% | | | | | | | | | | |
| 300 | 0.2 | 12.9 | 0.5 | 7.7 | | | | | | | | | | |
| 400 | 0.1 | 13.2 | 0.4 | 8.0 | 0.8% | 5.0% | | | | | | | | |
| 500 | 0.1 | 13.4 | 0.3 | 8.2 | 0.7 | 5.2 | | | | | | | | |
| 1,000 | 0.1 | 13.7 | 0.2 | 8.6 | 0.5 | 5.7 | 0.9% | 4.5% | 1.2% | 3.5% | | | | |
| 1,500 | 0.0* | 13.8 | 0.2 | 8.7 | 0.5 | 5.9 | 0.8 | 4.7 | 1.1 | 3.7 | | | | |
| 2,000 | 0.0* | 13.8 | 0.2 | 8.8 | 0.4 | 6.0 | 0.8 | 4.8 | 1.0 | 3.8 | 1.4% | 3.0% | | |
| 2,500 | 0.0* | 13.9 | 0.1 | 8.8 | 0.4 | 6.0 | 0.8 | 4.8 | 1.0 | 3.9 | 1.3 | 3.1 | | |
| 3,000 | 0.0* | 13.9 | 0.1 | 8.8 | 0.4 | 6.0 | 0.7 | 4.9 | 1.0 | 3.9 | 1.3 | 3.1 | | |
| 3,500 | 0.0* | 13.9 | 0.1 | 8.8 | 0.4 | 6.1 | 0.7 | 4.9 | 1.0 | 4.0 | 1.3 | 3.2 | | |
| 4,000 | 0.0* | 13.9 | 0.1 | 8.9 | 0.4 | 6.1 | 0.7 | 4.9 | 0.9 | 4.0 | 1.3 | 3.2 | 1.5% | 2.6% |
| 4,500 | 0.0* | 13.9 | 0.1 | 8.9 | 0.4 | 6.1 | 0.7 | 4.9 | 0.9 | 4.0 | 1.2 | 3.2 | 1.5 | 2.7 |
| 5,000 | 0.0* | 13.9 | 0.1 | 8.9 | 0.4 | 6.1 | 0.7 | 4.9 | 0.9 | 4.0 | 1.2 | 3.2 | 1.5 | 2.7 |
| 6,000 | 0.0* | 13.9 | 0.1 | 8.9 | 0.4 | 6.1 | 0.7 | 4.9 | 0.9 | 4.0 | 1.2 | 3.2 | 1.5 | 2.7 |
| 7,000 | 0.0* | 13.9 | 0.1 | 8.9 | 0.4 | 6.1 | 0.7 | 4.9 | 0.9 | 4.0 | 1.2 | 3.3 | 1.5 | 2.8 |
| 8,000 | 0.0* | 13.9 | 0.1 | 8.9 | 0.4 | 6.1 | 0.7 | 4.9 | 0.9 | 4.1 | 1.2 | 3.3 | 1.4 | 2.8 |
| 9,000 | 0.0* | 14.0 | 0.1 | 8.9 | 0.4 | 6.1 | 0.7 | 5.0 | 0.9 | 4.1 | 1.2 | 3.3 | 1.4 | 2.8 |
| 10,000 | 0.0* | 14.0 | 0.1 | 8.9 | 0.4 | 6.1 | 0.7 | 5.0 | 0.9 | 4.1 | 1.2 | 3.3 | 1.4 | 2.8 |
| 15,000 | 0.0* | 14.0 | 0.1 | 8.9 | 0.4 | 6.1 | 0.7 | 5.0 | 0.9 | 4.1 | 1.2 | 3.3 | 1.4 | 2.8 |
| 20,000 | 0.0* | 14.0 | 0.1 | 8.9 | 0.4 | 6.2 | 0.7 | 5.0 | 0.9 | 4.1 | 1.2 | 3.3 | 1.4 | 2.8 |
| 25,000 | 0.0* | 14.0 | 0.1 | 8.9 | 0.4 | 6.2 | 0.7 | 5.0 | 0.9 | 4.1 | 1.2 | 3.3 | 1.4 | 2.9 |
| 50,000 | 0.0* | 14.0 | 0.1 | 8.9 | 0.3 | 6.2 | 0.7 | 5.0 | 0.9 | 4.1 | 1.1 | 3.4 | 1.4 | 2.9 |
| 100,000 | 0.0* | 14.0 | 0.1 | 8.9 | 0.3 | 6.2 | 0.7 | 5.0 | 0.9 | 4.1 | 1.1 | 3.4 | 1.4 | 2.9 |

* Less than 0.05%

**SAMPLE RELIABILITY FOR RELATIVE FREQUENCIES**

**FOR RANDOM SAMPLES ONLY**

*Rate of Occurrence in Sample 3%*
*Confidence Level 99%*

*For Sample Size of:*

| *And Field Size is:* | 100 *Lower Limit* | 100 *Upper Limit* | 200 *Lower Limit* | 200 *Upper Limit* | 300 *Lower Limit* | 300 *Upper Limit* | 500 *Lower Limit* | 500 *Upper Limit* | 1000 *Lower Limit* | 1000 *Upper Limit* | 2000 *Lower Limit* | 2000 *Upper Limit* |
|---|---|---|---|---|---|---|---|---|---|---|---|---|
| 200 | 1.1% | 8.4% | | | | | | | | | | |
| 300 | 0.8 | 9.2 | | | | | | | | | | |
| 400 | 0.7 | 9.6 | 1.4% | 6.3% | | | | | | | | |
| 500 | 0.6 | 9.8 | 1.3 | 6.6 | | | | | | | | |
| 1,000 | 0.5 | 10.2 | 1.0 | 7.2 | 1.5% | 5.8% | 2.0% | 4.7% | | | | |
| 1,500 | 0.4 | 10.3 | 0.9 | 7.3 | 1.5 | 6.0 | 1.8 | 5.0 | | | | |
| 2,000 | 0.4 | 10.4 | 0.9 | 7.4 | 1.4 | 6.1 | 1.7 | 5.1 | 2.2% | 4.1% | | |
| 2,500 | 0.4 | 10.4 | 0.9 | 7.5 | 1.3 | 6.2 | 1.7 | 5.2 | 2.1 | 4.2 | | |
| 3,000 | 0.4 | 10.4 | 0.9 | 7.5 | 1.3 | 6.2 | 1.7 | 5.2 | 2.1 | 4.3 | | |
| 3,500 | 0.4 | 10.5 | 0.8 | 7.5 | 1.3 | 6.3 | 1.6 | 5.3 | 2.1 | 4.3 | | |
| 4,000 | 0.4 | 10.5 | 0.8 | 7.5 | 1.3 | 6.3 | 1.6 | 5.3 | 2.0 | 4.4 | 2.4% | 3.8% |
| 4,500 | 0.4 | 10.5 | 0.8 | 7.6 | 1.3 | 6.3 | 1.6 | 5.3 | 2.0 | 4.4 | 2.4 | 3.8 |
| 5,000 | 0.4 | 10.5 | 0.8 | 7.6 | 1.3 | 6.3 | 1.6 | 5.3 | 2.0 | 4.4 | 2.4 | 3.8 |
| 6,000 | 0.4 | 10.5 | 0.8 | 7.6 | 1.3 | 6.3 | 1.6 | 5.3 | 2.0 | 4.5 | 2.3 | 3.9 |
| 7,000 | 0.4 | 10.5 | 0.8 | 7.6 | 1.3 | 6.3 | 1.6 | 5.4 | 2.0 | 4.5 | 2.3 | 3.9 |
| 8,000 | 0.4 | 10.5 | 0.8 | 7.6 | 1.3 | 6.3 | 1.6 | 5.4 | 2.0 | 4.5 | 2.3 | 3.9 |
| 9,000 | 0.4 | 10.5 | 0.8 | 7.6 | 1.3 | 6.3 | 1.6 | 5.4 | 1.9 | 4.5 | 2.3 | 3.9 |
| 10,000 | 0.4 | 10.5 | 0.8 | 7.6 | 1.3 | 6.4 | 1.6 | 5.4 | 1.9 | 4.5 | 2.3 | 4.0 |
| 15,000 | 0.4 | 10.5 | 0.8 | 7.6 | 1.2 | 6.4 | 1.6 | 5.4 | 1.9 | 4.5 | 2.2 | 4.0 |
| 20,000 | 0.4 | 10.6 | 0.8 | 7.6 | 1.2 | 6.4 | 1.5 | 5.4 | 1.9 | 4.6 | 2.2 | 4.0 |
| 25,000 | 0.4 | 10.6 | 0.8 | 7.6 | 1.2 | 6.4 | 1.5 | 5.4 | 1.9 | 4.6 | 2.2 | 4.0 |
| 50,000 | 0.3 | 10.6 | 0.8 | 7.6 | 1.2 | 6.4 | 1.5 | 5.4 | 1.9 | 4.6 | 2.2 | 4.0 |
| 100,000 | 0.3 | 10.6 | 0.8 | 7.7 | 1.2 | 6.4 | 1.5 | 5.4 | 1.9 | 4.6 | 2.2 | 4.1 |

## SAMPLE RELIABILITY FOR RELATIVE FREQUENCIES

## FOR RANDOM SAMPLES ONLY

*Rate of Occurrence in Sample 4%*
*Confidence Level 99%*

*For Sample Size of:*

| *And Field Size is:* | 50 *Lower Limit* | 50 *Upper Limit* | 100 *Lower Limit* | 100 *Upper Limit* | 200 *Lower Limit* | 200 *Upper Limit* | 300 *Lower Limit* | 300 *Upper Limit* | 500 *Lower Limit* | 500 *Upper Limit* | 1000 *Lower Limit* | 1000 *Upper Limit* | 2000 *Lower Limit* | 2000 *Upper Limit* |
|---|---|---|---|---|---|---|---|---|---|---|---|---|---|---|
| 200 | 0.7% | 15.4% | 1.7% | 9.7% | | | | | | | | | | |
| 300 | 0.5 | 16.1 | 1.3 | 10.6 | | | | | | | | | | |
| 400 | 0.5 | 16.4 | 1.1 | 11.0 | 2.1% | 7.6% | | | | | | | | |
| 500 | 0.4 | 16.5 | 1.0 | 11.2 | 1.9 | 7.9 | | | | | | | | |
| 1,000 | 0.3 | 16.9 | 0.9 | 11.7 | 1.6 | 8.5 | 2.1% | 7.2% | 2.7% | 5.9% | | | | |
| 1,500 | 0.3 | 17.0 | 0.8 | 11.8 | 1.5 | 8.7 | 2.0 | 7.4 | 2.5 | 6.3 | | | | |
| 2,000 | 0.3 | 17.0 | 0.8 | 11.9 | 1.5 | 8.8 | 1.9 | 7.5 | 2.4 | 6.4 | 3.0% | 5.3% | | |
| 2,500 | 0.3 | 17.1 | 0.8 | 11.9 | 1.4 | 8.8 | 1.9 | 7.6 | 2.3 | 6.5 | 3.0 | 5.4 | | |
| 3,000 | 0.2 | 17.1 | 0.7 | 11.9 | 1.4 | 8.9 | 1.9 | 7.6 | 2.3 | 6.5 | 2.9 | 5.5 | | |
| 3,500 | 0.2 | 17.1 | 0.7 | 12.0 | 1.4 | 8.9 | 1.9 | 7.6 | 2.3 | 6.6 | 2.9 | 5.5 | | |
| 4,000 | 0.2 | 17.1 | 0.7 | 12.0 | 1.4 | 8.9 | 1.9 | 7.7 | 2.3 | 6.6 | 2.8 | 5.6 | 3.3% | 4.9% |
| 4,500 | 0.2 | 17.1 | 0.7 | 12.0 | 1.4 | 8.9 | 1.9 | 7.7 | 2.3 | 6.6 | 2.8 | 5.6 | 3.3 | 4.9 |
| 5,000 | 0.2 | 17.1 | 0.7 | 12.0 | 1.4 | 9.0 | 1.8 | 7.7 | 2.3 | 6.6 | 2.8 | 5.6 | 3.2 | 5.0 |
| 6,000 | 0.2 | 17.2 | 0.7 | 12.0 | 1.4 | 9.0 | 1.8 | 7.7 | 2.2 | 6.6 | 2.8 | 5.7 | 3.2 | 5.0 |
| 7,000 | 0.2 | 17.2 | 0.7 | 12.0 | 1.4 | 9.0 | 1.8 | 7.7 | 2.2 | 6.7 | 2.7 | 5.7 | 3.2 | 5.0 |
| 8,000 | 0.2 | 17.2 | 0.7 | 12.0 | 1.3 | 9.0 | 1.8 | 7.7 | 2.2 | 6.7 | 2.7 | 5.7 | 3.1 | 5.1 |
| 9,000 | 0.2 | 17.2 | 0.7 | 12.0 | 1.3 | 9.0 | 1.8 | 7.7 | 2.2 | 6.7 | 2.7 | 5.7 | 3.1 | 5.1 |
| 10,000 | 0.2 | 17.2 | 0.7 | 12.0 | 1.3 | 9.0 | 1.8 | 7.7 | 2.2 | 6.7 | 2.7 | 5.7 | 3.1 | 5.1 |
| 15,000 | 0.2 | 17.2 | 0.7 | 12.1 | 1.3 | 9.0 | 1.8 | 7.8 | 2.2 | 6.7 | 2.7 | 5.8 | 3.1 | 5.2 |
| 20,000 | 0.2 | 17.2 | 0.7 | 12.1 | 1.3 | 9.0 | 1.8 | 7.8 | 2.2 | 6.7 | 2.7 | 5.8 | 3.1 | 5.2 |
| 25,000 | 0.2 | 17.2 | 0.7 | 12.1 | 1.3 | 9.0 | 1.8 | 7.8 | 2.2 | 6.7 | 2.7 | 5.8 | 3.0 | 5.2 |
| 50,000 | 0.2 | 17.2 | 0.7 | 12.1 | 1.3 | 9.0 | 1.8 | 7.8 | 2.2 | 6.7 | 2.7 | 5.8 | 3.0 | 5.2 |
| 100,000 | 0.2 | 17.2 | 0.7 | 12.1 | 1.3 | 9.0 | 1.8 | 7.8 | 2.2 | 6.7 | 2.7 | 5.8 | 3.0 | 5.2 |

## SAMPLE RELIABILITY FOR RELATIVE FREQUENCIES

## FOR RANDOM SAMPLES ONLY

*Rate of Occurrence in Sample 5%*
*Confidence Level 99%*

*For Sample Size of:*

| *And Field Size is:* | 60 | | 100 | | 200 | | 300 | | 500 | | 1000 | | 2000 | |
|---|---|---|---|---|---|---|---|---|---|---|---|---|---|---|
| | *Lower Limit* | *Upper Limit* | *Lower Limit* | *Upper Limit* | *Lower Limit* | *Upper Limit* | *Lower Limit* | *Upper Limit* | *Lower Limit* | *Upper Limit* | *Lower Limit* | *Upper Limit* | *Lower Limit* | *Upper Limit* |
| 200 | 1.3% | 15.2% | 2.2% | 11.0% | | | | | | | | | | |
| 300 | 1.0 | 15.9 | 1.8 | 12.0 | | | | | | | | | | |
| 400 | 0.9 | 16.2 | 1.6 | 12.4 | 2.8% | 8.8% | | | | | | | | |
| 500 | 0.8 | 16.4 | 1.5 | 12.6 | 2.6 | 9.2 | | | | | | | | |
| 1,000 | 0.7 | 16.8 | 1.3 | 13.1 | 2.2 | 9.8 | 2.8% | 8.5% | 3.5% | 7.2% | | | | |
| 1,500 | 0.7 | 16.9 | 1.2 | 13.2 | 2.1 | 10.0 | 2.6 | 8.7 | 3.2 | 7.5 | | | | |
| 2,000 | 0.6 | 17.0 | 1.2 | 13.3 | 2.0 | 10.1 | 2.5 | 8.9 | 3.1 | 7.7 | 3.9% | 6.5% | | |
| 2,500 | 0.6 | 17.0 | 1.2 | 13.4 | 2.0 | 10.2 | 2.5 | 8.9 | 3.1 | 7.7 | 3.8 | 6.6 | | |
| 3,000 | 0.6 | 17.0 | 1.2 | 13.4 | 2.0 | 10.2 | 2.5 | 9.0 | 3.0 | 7.8 | 3.7 | 6.7 | | |
| 3,500 | 0.6 | 17.1 | 1.2 | 13.4 | 2.0 | 10.2 | 2.5 | 9.0 | 3.0 | 7.8 | 3.6 | 6.7 | | |
| 4,000 | 0.6 | 17.1 | 1.2 | 13.4 | 2.0 | 10.3 | 2.4 | 9.0 | 3.0 | 7.9 | 3.6 | 6.8 | 4.2% | 6.0% |
| 4,500 | 0.6 | 17.1 | 1.1 | 13.4 | 2.0 | 10.3 | 2.4 | 9.0 | 3.0 | 7.9 | 3.6 | 6.8 | 4.1 | 6.0 |
| 5,000 | 0.6 | 17.1 | 1.1 | 13.4 | 2.0 | 10.3 | 2.4 | 9.1 | 2.9 | 7.9 | 3.6 | 6.8 | 4.1 | 6.1 |
| 6,000 | 0.6 | 17.1 | 1.1 | 13.5 | 1.9 | 10.3 | 2.4 | 9.1 | 2.9 | 7.9 | 3.5 | 6.9 | 4.0 | 6.1 |
| 7,000 | 0.6 | 17.1 | 1.1 | 13.5 | 1.9 | 10.3 | 2.4 | 9.1 | 2.9 | 8.0 | 3.5 | 6.9 | 4.0 | 6.2 |
| 8,000 | 0.6 | 17.1 | 1.1 | 13.5 | 1.9 | 10.3 | 2.4 | 9.1 | 2.9 | 8.0 | 3.5 | 6.9 | 4.0 | 6.2 |
| 9,000 | 0.6 | 17.1 | 1.1 | 13.5 | 1.9 | 10.3 | 2.4 | 9.1 | 2.9 | 8.0 | 3.5 | 6.9 | 4.0 | 6.2 |
| 10,000 | 0.6 | 17.1 | 1.1 | 13.5 | 1.9 | 10.4 | 2.4 | 9.1 | 2.9 | 8.0 | 3.5 | 6.9 | 4.0 | 6.2 |
| 15,000 | 0.6 | 17.1 | 1.1 | 13.5 | 1.9 | 10.4 | 2.4 | 9.1 | 2.9 | 8.0 | 3.5 | 7.0 | 3.9 | 6.3 |
| 20,000 | 0.6 | 17.1 | 1.1 | 13.5 | 1.9 | 10.4 | 2.3 | 9.2 | 2.9 | 8.0 | 3.4 | 7.0 | 3.9 | 6.3 |
| 25,000 | 0.6 | 17.2 | 1.1 | 13.5 | 1.9 | 10.4 | 2.3 | 9.2 | 2.9 | 8.0 | 3.4 | 7.0 | 3.9 | 6.3 |
| 50,000 | 0.6 | 17.2 | 1.1 | 13.5 | 1.9 | 10.4 | 2.3 | 9.2 | 2.8 | 8.1 | 3.4 | 7.0 | 3.9 | 6.4 |
| 100,000 | 0.6 | 17.2 | 1.1 | 13.5 | 1.9 | 10.4 | 2.3 | 9.2 | 2.8 | 8.1 | 3.4 | 7.0 | 3.8 | 6.4 |

**SAMPLE RELIABILITY FOR RELATIVE FREQUENCIES**

**FOR RANDOM SAMPLES ONLY**

*Rate of Occurrence in Sample 6%*
*Confidence Level 99%*

*For Sample Size of:*

| And | 50 | | 100 | | 200 | | 300 | | 500 | | 1000 | | 2000 | |
|---|---|---|---|---|---|---|---|---|---|---|---|---|---|---|
| *Field Size is:* | *Lower Limit* | *Upper Limit* | *Lower Limit* | *Upper Limit* | *Lower Limit* | *Upper Limit* | *Lower Limit* | *Upper Limit* | *Lower Limit* | *Upper Limit* | *Lower Limit* | *Upper Limit* | *Lower Limit* | *Upper Limit* |
| 200 | 1.4% | 18.4% | 2.9% | 12.3% | | | | | | | | | | |
| 300 | 1.2 | 19.1 | 2.4 | 13.3 | | | | | | | | | | |
| 400 | 1.0 | 19.4 | 2.2 | 13.7 | 3.6% | 10.0% | | | | | | | | |
| 500 | 1.0 | 19.6 | 2.0 | 14.0 | 3.3 | 10.4 | | | | | | | | |
| 1,000 | 0.8 | 20.0 | 1.8 | 14.5 | 2.9 | 11.1 | 3.6% | 9.7% | 4.4% | 8.3% | | | | |
| 1,500 | 0.8 | 20.1 | 1.7 | 14.6 | 2.8 | 11.3 | 3.4 | 9.9 | 4.1 | 8.7 | | | | |
| 2,000 | 0.8 | 20.1 | 1.7 | 14.7 | 2.8 | 11.4 | 3.3 | 10.1 | 4.0 | 8.8 | 4.8% | 7.5% | | |
| 2,500 | 0.7 | 20.2 | 1.7 | 14.8 | 2.7 | 11.4 | 3.3 | 10.1 | 3.9 | 8.9 | 4.6 | 7.7 | | |
| 3,000 | 0.7 | 20.2 | 1.6 | 14.8 | 2.7 | 11.5 | 3.2 | 10.2 | 3.8 | 9.0 | 4.6 | 7.8 | | |
| 3,500 | 0.7 | 20.2 | 1.6 | 14.8 | 2.7 | 11.5 | 3.2 | 10.2 | 3.8 | 9.0 | 4.5 | 7.8 | | |
| 4,000 | 0.7 | 20.2 | 1.6 | 14.8 | 2.7 | 11.5 | 3.2 | 10.2 | 3.8 | 9.0 | 4.5 | 7.9 | 5.1% | 7.1% |
| 4,500 | 0.7 | 20.2 | 1.6 | 14.8 | 2.7 | 11.5 | 3.2 | 10.3 | 3.8 | 9.0 | 4.5 | 7.9 | 5.1 | 7.1 |
| 5,000 | 0.7 | 20.3 | 1.6 | 14.8 | 2.6 | 11.6 | 3.2 | 10.3 | 3.8 | 9.1 | 4.4 | 8.0 | 5.0 | 7.2 |
| 6,000 | 0.7 | 20.3 | 1.6 | 14.9 | 2.6 | 11.6 | 3.1 | 10.3 | 3.7 | 9.1 | 4.4 | 8.0 | 5.0 | 7.2 |
| 7,000 | 0.7 | 20.3 | 1.6 | 14.9 | 2.6 | 11.6 | 3.1 | 10.3 | 3.7 | 9.1 | 4.4 | 8.0 | 5.0 | 7.3 |
| 8,000 | 0.7 | 20.3 | 1.6 | 14.9 | 2.6 | 11.6 | 3.1 | 10.3 | 3.7 | 9.1 | 4.4 | 8.0 | 4.9 | 7.3 |
| 9,000 | 0.7 | 20.3 | 1.6 | 14.9 | 2.6 | 11.6 | 3.1 | 10.3 | 3.7 | 9.1 | 4.4 | 8.1 | 4.9 | 7.3 |
| 10,000 | 0.7 | 20.3 | 1.6 | 14.9 | 2.6 | 11.6 | 3.1 | 10.3 | 3.7 | 9.2 | 4.3 | 8.1 | 4.9 | 7.3 |
| 15,000 | 0.7 | 20.3 | 1.6 | 14.9 | 2.6 | 11.6 | 3.1 | 10.4 | 3.7 | 9.2 | 4.3 | 8.1 | 4.8 | 7.4 |
| 20,000 | 0.7 | 20.3 | 1.6 | 14.9 | 2.6 | 11.6 | 3.1 | 10.4 | 3.7 | 9.2 | 4.3 | 8.1 | 4.8 | 7.4 |
| 25,000 | 0.7 | 20.3 | 1.6 | 14.9 | 2.6 | 11.6 | 3.1 | 10.4 | 3.7 | 9.2 | 4.3 | 8.1 | 4.8 | 7.4 |
| 50,000 | 0.7 | 20.3 | 1.6 | 14.9 | 2.6 | 11.7 | 3.1 | 10.4 | 3.6 | 9.2 | 4.3 | 8.2 | 4.8 | 7.5 |
| 100,000 | 0.7 | 20.3 | 1.6 | 14.9 | 2.6 | 11.7 | 3.1 | 10.4 | 3.6 | 9.2 | 4.3 | 8.2 | 4.7 | 7.5 |

TABLE 6a (Continued)

## SAMPLE RELIABILITY FOR RELATIVE FREQUENCIES

## FOR RANDOM SAMPLES ONLY

*Rate of Occurrence in Sample 7%*
*Confidence Level 99%*

***For Sample Size of:***

| *And* | *100* | | *200* | | *300* | | *500* | | *1000* | | *2000* | |
|---|---|---|---|---|---|---|---|---|---|---|---|---|
| *Field Size is:* | *Lower Limit* | *Upper Limit* | *Lower Limit* | *Upper Limit* | *Lower Limit* | *Upper Limit* | *Lower Limit* | *Upper Limit* | *Lower Limit* | *Upper Limit* | *Lower Limit* | *Upper Limit* |
| 200 | 3.5% | 13.6% | | | | | | | | | | |
| 300 | 3.0 | 14.6 | | | | | | | | | | |
| 400 | 2.7 | 15.0 | 4.4% | 11.2% | | | | | | | | |
| 500 | 2.6 | 15.3 | 4.1 | 11.6 | | | | | | | | |
| 1,000 | 2.3 | 15.8 | 3.7 | 12.3 | 4.3% | 10.9% | 5.2% | 9.4% | | | | |
| 1,500 | 2.3 | 16.0 | 3.5 | 12.5 | 4.2 | 11.1 | 4.9 | 9.8 | | | | |
| 2,000 | 2.2 | 16.1 | 3.4 | 12.6 | 4.1 | 11.3 | 4.8 | 10.0 | 5.7% | 8.6% | | |
| 2,500 | 2.2 | 16.1 | 3.4 | 12.7 | 4.0 | 11.3 | 4.7 | 10.1 | 5.5 | 8.8 | | |
| 3,000 | 2.2 | 16.1 | 3.4 | 12.7 | 4.0 | 11.4 | 4.7 | 10.1 | 5.5 | 8.9 | | |
| 3,500 | 2.2 | 16.2 | 3.4 | 12.8 | 4.0 | 11.4 | 4.6 | 10.2 | 5.4 | 9.0 | | |
| 4,000 | 2.1 | 16.2 | 3.3 | 12.8 | 3.9 | 11.4 | 4.6 | 10.2 | 5.4 | 9.0 | 6.0% | 8.1% |
| 4,500 | 2.1 | 16.2 | 3.3 | 12.8 | 3.9 | 11.5 | 4.6 | 10.2 | 5.3 | 9.0 | 6.0 | 8.2 |
| 5,000 | 2.1 | 16.2 | 3.3 | 12.8 | 3.9 | 11.5 | 4.6 | 10.2 | 5.3 | 9.1 | 5.9 | 8.2 |
| 6,000 | 2.1 | 16.2 | 3.3 | 12.8 | 3.9 | 11.5 | 4.6 | 10.3 | 5.3 | 9.1 | 5.9 | 8.3 |
| 7,000 | 2.1 | 16.2 | 3.3 | 12.8 | 3.9 | 11.5 | 4.5 | 10.3 | 5.3 | 9.1 | 5.8 | 8.3 |
| 8,000 | 2.1 | 16.2 | 3.3 | 12.9 | 3.9 | 11.5 | 4.5 | 10.3 | 5.2 | 9.2 | 5.8 | 8.4 |
| 9,000 | 2.1 | 16.2 | 3.3 | 12.9 | 3.9 | 11.5 | 4.5 | 10.3 | 5.2 | 9.2 | 5.8 | 8.4 |
| 10,000 | 2.1 | 16.2 | 3.3 | 12.9 | 3.9 | 11.6 | 4.5 | 10.3 | 5.2 | 9.2 | 5.8 | 8.4 |
| 15,000 | 2.1 | 16.3 | 3.3 | 12.9 | 3.8 | 11.6 | 4.5 | 10.4 | 5.2 | 9.2 | 5.7 | 8.5 |
| 20,000 | 2.1 | 16.3 | 3.3 | 12.9 | 3.8 | 11.6 | 4.5 | 10.4 | 5.2 | 9.3 | 5.7 | 8.5 |
| 25,000 | 2.1 | 16.3 | 3.3 | 12.9 | 3.8 | 11.6 | 4.5 | 10.4 | 5.2 | 9.3 | 5.7 | 8.5 |
| 50,000 | 2.1 | 16.3 | 3.3 | 12.9 | 3.8 | 11.6 | 4.4 | 10.4 | 5.1 | 9.3 | 5.7 | 8.5 |
| 100,000 | 2.1 | 16.3 | 3.3 | 12.9 | 3.8 | 11.6 | 4.4 | 10.4 | 5.1 | 9.3 | 5.6 | 8.6 |

## SAMPLE RELIABILITY FOR RELATIVE FREQUENCIES
## FOR RANDOM SAMPLES ONLY

*Rate of Occurrence in Sample 8%*
*Confidence Level 99%*

*For Sample Size of:*

| *And Field Size is:* | 50 | | 100 | | 200 | | 300 | | 500 | | 1000 | | 2000 | |
|---|---|---|---|---|---|---|---|---|---|---|---|---|---|---|
| | *Lower Limit* | *Upper Limit* | *Lower Limit* | *Upper Limit* | *Lower Limit* | *Upper Limit* | *Lower Limit* | *Upper Limit* | *Lower Limit* | *Upper Limit* | *Lower Limit* | *Upper Limit* | *Lower Limit* | *Upper Limit* |
| 200 | 2.3% | 21.1% | 4.2% | 14.8% | | | | | | | | | | |
| 300 | 2.0 | 21.8 | 3.6 | 15.9 | | | | | | | | | | |
| 400 | 1.8 | 22.2 | 3.4 | 16.3 | 5.1% | 12.4% | | | | | | | | |
| 500 | 1.7 | 22.4 | 3.2 | 16.6 | 4.9 | 12.8 | | | | | | | | |
| 1,000 | 1.6 | 22.8 | 2.9 | 17.1 | 4.4 | 13.5 | 5.1% | 12.1% | 6.0% | 10.6% | | | | |
| 1,500 | 1.5 | 22.9 | 2.8 | 17.3 | 4.2 | 13.8 | 4.9 | 12.3 | 5.7 | 10.9 | | | | |
| 2,000 | 1.5 | 22.9 | 2.8 | 17.4 | 4.1 | 13.9 | 4.8 | 12.5 | 5.6 | 11.1 | 6.6% | 9.7% | | |
| 2,500 | 1.5 | 23.0 | 2.7 | 17.4 | 4.1 | 13.9 | 4.8 | 12.5 | 5.5 | 11.2 | 6.4 | 9.9 | | |
| 3,000 | 1.4 | 23.0 | 2.7 | 17.5 | 4.1 | 14.0 | 4.7 | 12.6 | 5.5 | 11.3 | 6.4 | 10.0 | | |
| 3,500 | 1.4 | 23.0 | 2.7 | 17.5 | 4.1 | 14.0 | 4.7 | 12.6 | 5.4 | 11.3 | 6.3 | 10.1 | | |
| 4,000 | 1.4 | 23.0 | 2.7 | 17.5 | 4.0 | 14.0 | 4.7 | 12.7 | 5.4 | 11.4 | 6.3 | 10.1 | 7.0% | 9.2% |
| 4,500 | 1.4 | 23.1 | 2.7 | 17.5 | 4.0 | 14.0 | 4.7 | 12.7 | 5.4 | 11.4 | 6.2 | 10.1 | 6.9 | 9.2 |
| 5,000 | 1.4 | 23.1 | 2.7 | 17.5 | 4.0 | 14.1 | 4.7 | 12.7 | 5.4 | 11.4 | 6.2 | 10.2 | 6.9 | 9.3 |
| 6,000 | 1.4 | 23.1 | 2.7 | 17.5 | 4.0 | 14.1 | 4.6 | 12.7 | 5.4 | 11.5 | 6.2 | 10.2 | 6.8 | 9.4 |
| 7,000 | 1.4 | 23.1 | 2.7 | 17.5 | 4.0 | 14.1 | 4.6 | 12.7 | 5.3 | 11.5 | 6.1 | 10.3 | 6.8 | 9.4 |
| 8,000 | 1.4 | 23.1 | 2.7 | 17.6 | 4.0 | 14.1 | 4.6 | 12.8 | 5.3 | 11.5 | 6.1 | 10.3 | 6.7 | 9.5 |
| 9,000 | 1.4 | 23.1 | 2.7 | 17.6 | 4.0 | 14.1 | 4.6 | 12.8 | 5.3 | 11.5 | 6.1 | 10.3 | 6.7 | 9.5 |
| 10,000 | 1.4 | 23.1 | 2.7 | 17.6 | 4.0 | 14.1 | 4.6 | 12.8 | 5.3 | 11.5 | 6.1 | 10.3 | 6.7 | 9.5 |
| 15,000 | 1.4 | 23.1 | 2.7 | 17.6 | 4.0 | 14.1 | 4.6 | 12.8 | 5.3 | 11.5 | 6.1 | 10.4 | 6.6 | 9.6 |
| 20,000 | 1.4 | 23.1 | 2.6 | 17.6 | 4.0 | 14.2 | 4.6 | 12.8 | 5.3 | 11.6 | 6.0 | 10.4 | 6.6 | 9.6 |
| 25,000 | 1.4 | 23.1 | 2.6 | 17.6 | 4.0 | 14.2 | 4.6 | 12.8 | 5.3 | 11.6 | 6.0 | 10.4 | 6.6 | 9.6 |
| 50,000 | 1.4 | 23.1 | 2.6 | 17.6 | 3.9 | 14.2 | 4.6 | 12.8 | 5.2 | 11.6 | 6.0 | 10.4 | 6.6 | 9.6 |
| 100,000 | 1.4 | 23.1 | 2.6 | 17.6 | 3.9 | 14.2 | 4.6 | 12.8 | 5.2 | 11.6 | 6.0 | 10.4 | 6.6 | 9.7 |

## SAMPLE RELIABILITY FOR RELATIVE FREQUENCIES
## FOR RANDOM SAMPLES ONLY

*Rate of Occurrence in Sample 9%*
*Confidence Level 99%*

| *And Field Size is:* | *For Sample Size of:* 100 *Lower Limit* | *Upper Limit* | 200 *Lower Limit* | *Upper Limit* | 300 *Lower Limit* | *Upper Limit* | 500 *Lower Limit* | *Upper Limit* | 1000 *Lower Limit* | *Upper Limit* | 2000 *Lower Limit* | *Upper Limit* |
|---|---|---|---|---|---|---|---|---|---|---|---|---|
| 200 | 4.9% | 16.0% | | | | | | | | | | |
| 300 | 4.3 | 17.1 | | | | | | | | | | |
| 400 | 4.0 | 17.6 | 5.9% | 13.6% | | | | | | | | |
| 500 | 3.8 | 17.9 | 5.6 | 14.0 | | | | | | | | |
| 1,000 | 3.5 | 18.4 | 5.1 | 14.8 | 5.9% | 13.2% | 6.9% | 11.7% | | | | |
| 1,500 | 3.4 | 18.6 | 4.9 | 15.0 | 5.7 | 13.5 | 6.6 | 12.1 | | | | |
| 2,000 | 3.4 | 18.7 | 4.8 | 15.1 | 5.6 | 13.7 | 6.4 | 12.3 | 7.5% | 10.8% | | |
| 2,500 | 3.3 | 18.7 | 4.8 | 15.2 | 5.5 | 13.8 | 6.4 | 12.4 | 7.3 | 11.0 | | |
| 3,000 | 3.3 | 18.8 | 4.8 | 15.2 | 5.5 | 13.8 | 6.3 | 12.4 | 7.2 | 11.1 | | |
| 3,500 | 3.3 | 18.8 | 4.7 | 15.3 | 5.5 | 13.8 | 6.3 | 12.5 | 7.2 | 11.2 | | |
| 4,000 | 3.3 | 18.8 | 4.7 | 15.3 | 5.4 | 13.9 | 6.2 | 12.6 | 7.1 | 11.2 | 7.9% | 10.2% |
| 4,500 | 3.3 | 18.8 | 4.7 | 15.3 | 5.4 | 13.9 | 6.2 | 12.6 | 7.1 | 11.3 | 7.8 | 10.3 |
| 5,000 | 3.3 | 18.8 | 4.7 | 15.3 | 5.4 | 13.9 | 6.2 | 12.6 | 7.1 | 11.3 | 7.8 | 10.4 |
| 6,000 | 3.3 | 18.8 | 4.7 | 15.3 | 5.4 | 13.9 | 6.2 | 12.6 | 7.0 | 11.3 | 7.7 | 10.4 |
| 7,000 | 3.3 | 18.9 | 4.7 | 15.4 | 5.4 | 14.0 | 6.2 | 12.6 | 7.0 | 11.4 | 7.7 | 10.5 |
| 8,000 | 3.3 | 18.9 | 4.7 | 15.4 | 5.4 | 14.0 | 6.1 | 12.7 | 7.0 | 11.4 | 7.7 | 10.5 |
| 9,000 | 3.2 | 18.9 | 4.7 | 15.4 | 5.4 | 14.0 | 6.1 | 12.7 | 7.0 | 11.4 | 7.6 | 10.6 |
| 10,000 | 3.2 | 18.9 | 4.7 | 15.4 | 5.4 | 14.0 | 6.1 | 12.7 | 7.0 | 11.4 | 7.6 | 10.6 |
| 15,000 | 3.2 | 18.9 | 4.6 | 15.4 | 5.3 | 14.0 | 6.1 | 12.7 | 6.9 | 11.5 | 7.6 | 10.6 |
| 20,000 | 3.2 | 18.9 | 4.6 | 15.4 | 5.3 | 14.0 | 6.1 | 12.7 | 6.9 | 11.5 | 7.5 | 10.7 |
| 25,000 | 3.2 | 18.9 | 4.6 | 15.4 | 5.3 | 14.0 | 6.1 | 12.7 | 6.9 | 11.5 | 7.5 | 10.7 |
| 50,000 | 3.2 | 18.9 | 4.6 | 15.4 | 5.3 | 14.0 | 6.1 | 12.7 | 6.9 | 11.5 | 7.5 | 10.7 |
| 100,000 | 3.2 | 18.9 | 4.6 | 15.4 | 5.3 | 14.1 | 6.1 | 12.8 | 6.9 | 11.6 | 7.5 | 10.7 |

TABLE 6a (Continued)

## SAMPLE RELIABILITY FOR RELATIVE FREQUENCIES

## FOR RANDOM SAMPLES ONLY

*Rate of Occurrence in Sample 10%*
*Confidence Level 99%*

| And | For Sample Size of: 50 | | 100 | | 200 | | 300 | | 500 | | 1000 | | 2000 | |
|---|---|---|---|---|---|---|---|---|---|---|---|---|---|---|
| Field Size is: | Lower Limit | Upper Limit | Lower Limit | Upper Limit | Lower Limit | Upper Limit | Lower Limit | Upper Limit | Lower Limit | Upper Limit | Lower Limit | Upper Limit | Lower Limit | Upper Limit |
| 200 | 3.3% | 23.7% | 5.6% | 17.2% | | | | | | | | | | |
| 300 | 2.9 | 24.4 | 5.0 | 18.3 | | | | | | | | | | |
| 400 | 2.7 | 24.8 | 4.6 | 18.8 | 6.7% | 14.7% | | | | | | | | |
| 500 | 2.6 | 25.0 | 4.5 | 19.1 | 6.4 | 15.2 | | | | | | | | |
| 1,000 | 2.4 | 25.4 | 4.1 | 19.7 | 5.8 | 16.0 | 6.7% | 14.4% | 7.8% | 12.8% | | | | |
| 1,500 | 2.4 | 25.5 | 4.0 | 19.9 | 5.6 | 16.2 | 6.5 | 14.7 | 7.4 | 13.2 | | | | |
| 2,000 | 2.3 | 25.6 | 4.0 | 19.9 | 5.5 | 16.4 | 6.4 | 14.9 | 7.3 | 13.4 | 8.4% | 11.9% | | |
| 2,500 | 2.3 | 25.6 | 3.9 | 20.0 | 5.5 | 16.4 | 6.3 | 15.0 | 7.2 | 13.5 | 8.2 | 12.1 | | |
| 3,000 | 2.3 | 25.7 | 3.9 | 20.0 | 5.5 | 16.5 | 6.2 | 15.0 | 7.1 | 13.6 | 8.1 | 12.2 | | |
| 3,500 | 2.3 | 25.7 | 3.9 | 20.1 | 5.4 | 16.5 | 6.2 | 15.1 | 7.1 | 13.7 | 8.1 | 12.3 | | |
| 4,000 | 2.3 | 25.7 | 3.9 | 20.1 | 5.4 | 16.5 | 6.2 | 15.1 | 7.0 | 13.7 | 8.0 | 12.3 | 8.8% | 11.3% |
| 4,500 | 2.3 | 25.7 | 3.9 | 20.1 | 5.4 | 16.6 | 6.2 | 15.1 | 7.0 | 13.7 | 8.0 | 12.4 | 8.8 | 11.4 |
| 5,000 | 2.3 | 25.7 | 3.9 | 20.1 | 5.4 | 16.6 | 6.2 | 15.1 | 7.0 | 13.7 | 7.9 | 12.4 | 8.7 | 11.4 |
| 6,000 | 2.3 | 25.7 | 3.9 | 20.1 | 5.4 | 16.6 | 6.1 | 15.2 | 7.0 | 13.8 | 7.9 | 12.5 | 8.7 | 11.5 |
| 7,000 | 2.3 | 25.7 | 3.9 | 20.1 | 5.4 | 16.6 | 6.1 | 15.2 | 7.0 | 13.8 | 7.9 | 12.5 | 8.6 | 11.6 |
| 8,000 | 2.2 | 25.8 | 3.9 | 20.1 | 5.4 | 16.6 | 6.1 | 15.2 | 6.9 | 13.8 | 7.9 | 12.5 | 8.6 | 11.6 |
| 9,000 | 2.2 | 25.8 | 3.9 | 20.1 | 5.3 | 16.6 | 6.1 | 15.2 | 6.9 | 13.8 | 7.8 | 12.5 | 8.5 | 11.6 |
| 10,000 | 2.2 | 25.8 | 3.9 | 20.2 | 5.3 | 16.6 | 6.1 | 15.2 | 6.9 | 13.9 | 7.8 | 12.6 | 8.5 | 11.7 |
| 15,000 | 2.2 | 25.8 | 3.8 | 20.2 | 5.3 | 16.7 | 6.1 | 15.2 | 6.9 | 13.9 | 7.8 | 12.6 | 8.5 | 11.7 |
| 20,000 | 2.2 | 25.8 | 3.8 | 20.2 | 5.3 | 16.7 | 6.1 | 15.2 | 6.9 | 13.9 | 7.8 | 12.6 | 8.4 | 11.8 |
| 25,000 | 2.2 | 25.8 | 3.8 | 20.2 | 5.3 | 16.7 | 6.1 | 15.3 | 6.9 | 13.9 | 7.8 | 12.6 | 8.4 | 11.8 |
| 50,000 | 2.2 | 25.8 | 3.8 | 20.2 | 5.3 | 16.7 | 6.1 | 15.3 | 6.9 | 13.9 | 7.7 | 12.7 | 8.4 | 11.8 |
| 100,000 | 2.2 | 25.8 | 3.8 | 20.2 | 5.3 | 16.7 | 6.0 | 15.3 | 6.9 | 13.9 | 7.7 | 12.7 | 8.4 | 11.8 |

## SAMPLE RELIABILITY FOR RELATIVE FREQUENCIES
## FOR RANDOM SAMPLES ONLY

*Rate of Occurrence in Sample 11%*
*Confidence Level 99%*

*For Sample Size of:*

| *And Field Size is:* | 100 *Lower Limit* | 100 *Upper Limit* | 200 *Lower Limit* | 200 *Upper Limit* | 300 *Lower Limit* | 300 *Upper Limit* | 500 *Lower Limit* | 500 *Upper Limit* | 1000 *Lower Limit* | 1000 *Upper Limit* | 2000 *Lower Limit* | 2000 *Upper Limit* |
|---|---|---|---|---|---|---|---|---|---|---|---|---|
| 200 | 6.4% | 18.4% | | | | | | | | | | |
| 300 | 5.7 | 19.5 | | | | | | | | | | |
| 400 | 5.4 | 20.0 | 7.5% | 15.9% | | | | | | | | |
| 500 | 5.2 | 20.3 | 7.2 | 16.3 | | | | | | | | |
| 1,000 | 4.8 | 20.9 | 6.6 | 17.1 | 7.5% | 15.5% | 8.7% | 13.9% | | | | |
| 1,500 | 4.7 | 21.1 | 6.4 | 17.4 | 7.3 | 15.9 | 8.3 | 14.3 | | | | |
| 2,000 | 4.6 | 21.2 | 6.3 | 17.5 | 7.2 | 16.0 | 8.1 | 14.5 | 9.3% | 13.0% | | |
| 2,500 | 4.6 | 21.2 | 6.3 | 17.6 | 7.1 | 16.1 | 8.1 | 14.6 | 9.1 | 13.2 | | |
| 3,000 | 4.6 | 21.2 | 6.2 | 17.6 | 7.1 | 16.2 | 8.0 | 14.7 | 9.0 | 13.3 | | |
| 3,500 | 4.6 | 21.3 | 6.2 | 17.7 | 7.0 | 16.2 | 7.9 | 14.8 | 9.0 | 13.4 | | |
| 4,000 | 4.6 | 21.3 | 6.2 | 17.7 | 7.0 | 16.2 | 7.9 | 14.8 | 8.9 | 13.4 | 9.8% | 12.4% |
| 4,500 | 4.6 | 21.3 | 6.2 | 17.7 | 7.0 | 16.3 | 7.9 | 14.8 | 8.9 | 13.5 | 9.7 | 12.4 |
| 5,000 | 4.6 | 21.3 | 6.2 | 17.7 | 7.0 | 16.3 | 7.9 | 14.9 | 8.9 | 13.5 | 9.7 | 12.5 |
| 6,000 | 4.5 | 21.3 | 6.1 | 17.8 | 7.0 | 16.3 | 7.8 | 14.9 | 8.8 | 13.5 | 9.6 | 12.6 |
| 7,000 | 4.5 | 21.3 | 6.1 | 17.8 | 6.9 | 16.3 | 7.8 | 14.9 | 8.8 | 13.6 | 9.6 | 12.6 |
| 8,000 | 4.5 | 21.4 | 6.1 | 17.8 | 6.9 | 16.3 | 7.8 | 14.9 | 8.8 | 13.6 | 9.5 | 12.7 |
| 9,000 | 4.5 | 21.4 | 6.1 | 17.8 | 6.9 | 16.3 | 7.8 | 15.0 | 8.7 | 13.6 | 9.5 | 12.7 |
| 10,000 | 4.5 | 21.4 | 6.1 | 17.8 | 6.9 | 16.4 | 7.8 | 15.0 | 8.7 | 13.6 | 9.5 | 12.7 |
| 15,000 | 4.5 | 21.4 | 6.1 | 17.8 | 6.9 | 16.4 | 7.8 | 15.0 | 8.7 | 13.7 | 9.4 | 12.8 |
| 20,000 | 4.5 | 21.4 | 6.1 | 17.8 | 6.9 | 16.4 | 7.8 | 15.0 | 8.7 | 13.7 | 9.4 | 12.8 |
| 25,000 | 4.5 | 21.4 | 6.1 | 17.8 | 6.9 | 16.4 | 7.7 | 15.0 | 8.7 | 13.7 | 9.4 | 12.8 |
| 50,000 | 4.5 | 21.4 | 6.1 | 17.9 | 6.9 | 16.4 | 7.7 | 15.1 | 8.6 | 13.8 | 9.3 | 12.9 |
| 100,000 | 4.5 | 21.4 | 6.1 | 17.9 | 6.9 | 16.4 | 7.7 | 15.1 | 8.6 | 13.8 | 9.3 | 12.9 |

**SAMPLE RELIABILITY FOR RELATIVE FREQUENCIES**

**FOR RANDOM SAMPLES ONLY**

*Rate of Occurrence in Sample 12%*
*Confidence Level 99%*

| And Field Size is: | For Sample Size of: 50 Lower Limit | 50 Upper Limit | 100 Lower Limit | 100 Upper Limit | 200 Lower Limit | 200 Upper Limit | 300 Lower Limit | 300 Upper Limit | 500 Lower Limit | 500 Upper Limit | 1000 Lower Limit | 1000 Upper Limit | 2000 Lower Limit | 2000 Upper Limit |
|---|---|---|---|---|---|---|---|---|---|---|---|---|---|---|
| 200 | 4.4 | 26.2% | 7.2% | 19.5% | | | | | | | | | | |
| 300 | 4.0 | 27.0 | 6.4 | 20.7 | | | | | | | | | | |
| 400 | 3.8 | 27.4 | 6.1 | 21.2 | 8.3% | 17.0% | | | | | | | | |
| 500 | 3.6 | 27.6 | 5.9 | 21.5 | 8.0 | 17.5 | | | | | | | | |
| 1,000 | 3.4 | 28.0 | 5.5 | 22.1 | 7.4 | 18.3 | 8.4% | 16.7% | 9.6% | 15.0% | | | | |
| 1,500 | 3.3 | 28.1 | 5.4 | 22.3 | 7.2 | 18.6 | 8.1 | 17.0 | 9.2 | 15.4 | | | | |
| 2,000 | 3.3 | 28.2 | 5.3 | 22.4 | 7.1 | 18.7 | 8.0 | 17.1 | 9.0 | 15.6 | 10.2% | 14.0% | | |
| 2,500 | 3.3 | 28.3 | 5.3 | 22.4 | 7.0 | 18.8 | 7.9 | 17.2 | 8.9 | 15.8 | 10.1 | 14.2 | | |
| 3,000 | 3.3 | 28.3 | 5.3 | 22.5 | 7.0 | 18.8 | 7.9 | 17.3 | 8.9 | 15.8 | 10.0 | 14.3 | | |
| 3,500 | 3.2 | 28.3 | 5.3 | 22.5 | 7.0 | 18.9 | 7.9 | 17.3 | 8.8 | 15.9 | 9.9 | 14.4 | | |
| 4,000 | 3.2 | 28.3 | 5.2 | 22.5 | 7.0 | 18.9 | 7.8 | 17.4 | 8.8 | 15.9 | 9.8 | 14.5 | 10.7% | 13.4% |
| 4,500 | 3.2 | 28.3 | 5.2 | 22.5 | 7.0 | 18.9 | 7.8 | 17.4 | 8.8 | 16.0 | 9.8 | 14.5 | 10.7 | 13.5 |
| 5,000 | 3.2 | 28.3 | 5.2 | 22.5 | 6.9 | 18.9 | 7.8 | 17.4 | 8.7 | 16.0 | 9.8 | 14.6 | 10.6 | 13.5 |
| 6,000 | 3.2 | 28.4 | 5.2 | 22.6 | 6.9 | 18.9 | 7.8 | 17.4 | 8.7 | 16.0 | 9.7 | 14.6 | 10.5 | 13.6 |
| 7,000 | 3.2 | 28.4 | 5.2 | 22.6 | 6.9 | 19.0 | 7.8 | 17.5 | 8.7 | 16.0 | 9.7 | 14.7 | 10.5 | 13.7 |
| 8,000 | 3.2 | 28.4 | 5.2 | 22.6 | 6.9 | 19.0 | 7.8 | 17.5 | 8.7 | 16.1 | 9.7 | 14.7 | 10.5 | 13.7 |
| 9,000 | 3.2 | 28.4 | 5.2 | 22.6 | 6.9 | 19.0 | 7.7 | 17.5 | 8.7 | 16.1 | 9.7 | 14.7 | 10.4 | 13.8 |
| 10,000 | 3.2 | 28.4 | 5.2 | 22.6 | 6.9 | 19.0 | 7.7 | 17.5 | 8.7 | 16.1 | 9.6 | 14.7 | 10.4 | 13.8 |
| 15,000 | 3.2 | 28.4 | 5.2 | 22.6 | 6.9 | 19.0 | 7.7 | 17.5 | 8.6 | 16.1 | 9.6 | 14.8 | 10.3 | 13.8 |
| 20,000 | 3.2 | 28.4 | 5.2 | 22.6 | 6.9 | 19.0 | 7.7 | 17.5 | 8.6 | 16.1 | 9.6 | 14.8 | 10.3 | 13.9 |
| 25,000 | 3.2 | 28.4 | 5.2 | 22.6 | 6.9 | 19.0 | 7.7 | 17.6 | 8.6 | 16.2 | 9.6 | 14.8 | 10.3 | 13.9 |
| 50,000 | 3.2 | 28.4 | 5.2 | 22.6 | 6.8 | 19.0 | 7.7 | 17.6 | 8.6 | 16.2 | 9.5 | 14.8 | 10.3 | 13.9 |
| 100,000 | 3.2 | 28.4 | 5.2 | 22.6 | 6.8 | 19.0 | 7.7 | 17.6 | 8.6 | 16.2 | 9.5 | 14.9 | 10.2 | 14.0 |

## SAMPLE RELIABILITY FOR RELATIVE FREQUENCIES

## FOR RANDOM SAMPLES ONLY

*Rate of Occurrence in Sample 13%*
*Confidence Level 99%*

*For Sample Size of:*

| *And Field Size is:* | 100 | | 200 | | 300 | | 500 | | 1000 | | 2000 | |
|---|---|---|---|---|---|---|---|---|---|---|---|---|
| | *Lower Limit* | *Upper Limit* | *Lower Limit* | *Upper Limit* | *Lower Limit* | *Upper Limit* | *Lower Limit* | *Upper Limit* | *Lower Limit* | *Upper Limit* | *Lower Limit* | *Upper Limit* |
| 200 | 7.9% | 20.7% | | | | | | | | | | |
| 300 | 7.1 | 21.9 | | | | | | | | | | |
| 400 | 6.8 | 22.4 | 9.2% | 18.1% | | | | | | | | |
| 500 | 6.6 | 22.7 | 8.8 | 18.6 | | | | | | | | |
| 1,000 | 6.2 | 23.3 | 8.2 | 19.5 | 9.2% | 17.8% | 10.5% | 16.1% | | | | |
| 1,500 | 6.1 | 23.5 | 7.9 | 19.7 | 9.0 | 18.1 | 10.1 | 16.5 | | | | |
| 2,000 | 6.0 | 23.6 | 7.9 | 19.9 | 8.8 | 18.3 | 9.9 | 16.7 | 11.2% | 15.1% | | |
| 2,500 | 6.0 | 23.7 | 7.8 | 19.9 | 8.8 | 18.4 | 9.8 | 16.9 | 11.0 | 15.3 | | |
| 3,000 | 5.9 | 23.7 | 7.8 | 20.0 | 8.7 | 18.4 | 9.7 | 16.9 | 10.9 | 15.4 | | |
| 3,500 | 5.9 | 23.7 | 7.8 | 20.0 | 8.7 | 18.5 | 9.7 | 17.0 | 10.8 | 15.5 | | |
| 4,000 | 5.9 | 23.7 | 7.7 | 20.1 | 8.7 | 18.5 | 9.7 | 17.0 | 10.8 | 15.6 | 11.7% | 14.4% |
| 4,500 | 5.9 | 23.8 | 7.7 | 20.1 | 8.6 | 18.5 | 9.6 | 17.1 | 10.7 | 15.6 | 11.6 | 14.5 |
| 5,000 | 5.9 | 23.8 | 7.7 | 20.1 | 8.6 | 18.6 | 9.6 | 17.1 | 10.7 | 15.6 | 11.6 | 14.6 |
| 6,000 | 5.9 | 23.8 | 7.7 | 20.1 | 8.6 | 18.6 | 9.6 | 17.1 | 10.6 | 15.7 | 11.5 | 14.7 |
| 7,000 | 5.9 | 23.8 | 7.7 | 20.1 | 8.6 | 18.6 | 9.6 | 17.2 | 10.6 | 15.7 | 11.4 | 14.7 |
| 8,000 | 5.9 | 23.8 | 7.7 | 20.1 | 8.6 | 18.6 | 9.5 | 17.2 | 10.6 | 15.8 | 11.4 | 14.8 |
| 9,000 | 5.9 | 23.8 | 7.7 | 20.2 | 8.6 | 18.6 | 9.5 | 17.2 | 10.6 | 15.8 | 11.4 | 14.8 |
| 10,000 | 5.9 | 23.8 | 7.7 | 20.2 | 8.6 | 18.6 | 9.5 | 17.2 | 10.5 | 15.8 | 11.3 | 14.8 |
| 15,000 | 5.8 | 23.8 | 7.6 | 20.2 | 8.5 | 18.7 | 9.5 | 17.2 | 10.5 | 15.9 | 11.3 | 14.9 |
| 20,000 | 5.8 | 23.9 | 7.6 | 20.2 | 8.5 | 18.7 | 9.5 | 17.3 | 10.5 | 15.9 | 11.2 | 14.9 |
| 25,000 | 5.8 | 23.9 | 7.6 | 20.2 | 8.5 | 18.7 | 9.5 | 17.3 | 10.5 | 15.9 | 11.2 | 15.0 |
| 50,000 | 5.8 | 23.9 | 7.6 | 20.2 | 8.5 | 18.7 | 9.4 | 17.3 | 10.4 | 15.9 | 11.2 | 15.0 |
| 100,000 | 5.8 | 23.9 | 7.6 | 20.2 | 8.5 | 18.7 | 9.4 | 17.3 | 10.4 | 15.9 | 11.2 | 15.0 |

## SAMPLE RELIABILITY FOR RELATIVE FREQUENCIES
## FOR RANDOM SAMPLES ONLY

*Rate of Occurrence in Sample 14%*
*Confidence Level 99%*

| *And Field Size is:* | *For Sample Size of:* 50 *Lower Limit* | 50 *Upper Limit* | 100 *Lower Limit* | 100 *Upper Limit* | 200 *Lower Limit* | 200 *Upper Limit* | 300 *Lower Limit* | 300 *Upper Limit* | 500 *Lower Limit* | 500 *Upper Limit* | 1000 *Lower Limit* | 1000 *Upper Limit* | 2000 *Lower Limit* | 2000 *Upper Limit* |
|---|---|---|---|---|---|---|---|---|---|---|---|---|---|---|
| 200 | 5.6% | 28.7% | 8.7% | 21.9% | | | | | | | | | | |
| 300 | 5.1 | 29.5 | 7.9 | 23.1 | | | | | | | | | | |
| 400 | 4.9 | 29.8 | 7.5 | 23.6 | 10.0% | 19.2% | | | | | | | | |
| 500 | 4.8 | 30.1 | 7.3 | 23.9 | 9.7 | 19.7 | | | | | | | | |
| 1,000 | 4.5 | 30.5 | 6.9 | 24.5 | 9.0 | 20.6 | 10.1% | 18.9% | 11.4% | 17.1% | | | | |
| 1,500 | 4.4 | 30.6 | 6.7 | 24.7 | 8.8 | 20.9 | 9.8 | 19.3 | 11.0 | 17.6 | | | | |
| 2,000 | 4.4 | 30.7 | 6.7 | 24.8 | 8.7 | 21.0 | 9.7 | 19.4 | 10.8 | 17.8 | 12.1% | 16.2% | | |
| 2,500 | 4.4 | 30.8 | 6.6 | 24.9 | 8.6 | 21.1 | 9.6 | 19.5 | 10.7 | 18.0 | 11.9 | 16.4 | | |
| 3,000 | 4.3 | 30.8 | 6.6 | 24.9 | 8.6 | 21.2 | 9.5 | 19.6 | 10.6 | 18.0 | 11.8 | 16.5 | | |
| 3,500 | 4.3 | 30.8 | 6.6 | 24.9 | 8.5 | 21.2 | 9.5 | 19.6 | 10.6 | 18.1 | 11.7 | 16.6 | | |
| 4,000 | 4.3 | 30.8 | 6.6 | 25.0 | 8.5 | 21.2 | 9.5 | 19.7 | 10.5 | 18.1 | 11.7 | 16.6 | 12.6% | 15.5% |
| 4,500 | 4.3 | 30.8 | 6.6 | 25.0 | 8.5 | 21.2 | 9.5 | 19.7 | 10.5 | 18.2 | 11.6 | 16.7 | 12.6 | 15.6 |
| 5,000 | 4.3 | 30.8 | 6.6 | 25.0 | 8.5 | 21.3 | 9.4 | 19.7 | 10.5 | 18.2 | 11.6 | 16.7 | 12.5 | 15.6 |
| 6,000 | 4.3 | 30.9 | 6.5 | 25.0 | 8.5 | 21.3 | 9.4 | 19.7 | 10.4 | 18.2 | 11.5 | 16.8 | 12.4 | 15.7 |
| 7,000 | 4.3 | 30.9 | 6.5 | 25.0 | 8.5 | 21.3 | 9.4 | 19.8 | 10.4 | 18.3 | 11.5 | 16.8 | 12.4 | 15.8 |
| 8,000 | 4.3 | 30.9 | 6.5 | 25.0 | 8.5 | 21.3 | 9.4 | 19.8 | 10.4 | 18.3 | 11.5 | 16.8 | 12.3 | 15.8 |
| 9,000 | 4.3 | 30.9 | 6.5 | 25.0 | 8.4 | 21.3 | 9.4 | 19.8 | 10.4 | 18.3 | 11.5 | 16.9 | 12.3 | 15.9 |
| 10,000 | 4.3 | 30.9 | 6.5 | 25.0 | 8.4 | 21.3 | 9.4 | 19.8 | 10.4 | 18.3 | 11.5 | 16.9 | 12.3 | 15.9 |
| 15,000 | 4.3 | 30.9 | 6.5 | 25.1 | 8.4 | 21.4 | 9.4 | 19.8 | 10.3 | 18.4 | 11.4 | 16.9 | 12.2 | 16.0 |
| 20,000 | 4.3 | 30.9 | 6.5 | 25.1 | 8.4 | 21.4 | 9.3 | 19.8 | 10.3 | 18.4 | 11.4 | 17.0 | 12.2 | 16.0 |
| 25,000 | 4.3 | 30.9 | 6.5 | 25.1 | 8.4 | 21.4 | 9.3 | 19.8 | 10.3 | 18.4 | 11.4 | 17.0 | 12.2 | 16.0 |
| 50,000 | 4.3 | 30.9 | 6.5 | 25.1 | 8.4 | 21.4 | 9.3 | 19.9 | 10.3 | 18.4 | 11.3 | 17.0 | 12.1 | 16.1 |
| 100,000 | 4.3 | 30.9 | 6.5 | 25.1 | 8.4 | 21.4 | 9.3 | 19.9 | 10.3 | 18.4 | 11.3 | 17.0 | 12.1 | 16.1 |

TABLE 6a (Continued)

**SAMPLE RELIABILITY FOR RELATIVE FREQUENCIES**

**FOR RANDOM SAMPLES ONLY**

*Rate of Occurrence in Sample 15%*
*Confidence Level 99%*

| *And Field Size is:* | *For Sample Size of:* 50 | | 100 | | 200 | | 300 | | 500 | | 1000 | | 2000 | |
|---|---|---|---|---|---|---|---|---|---|---|---|---|---|---|
| | *Lower Limit* | *Upper Limit* | *Lower Limit* | *Upper Limit* | *Lower Limit* | *Upper Limit* | *Lower Limit* | *Upper Limit* | *Lower Limit* | *Upper Limit* | *Lower Limit* | *Upper Limit* | *Lower Limit* | *Upper Limit* |
| 200 | 7.0% | 27.9% | 9.5% | 23.0% | | | | | | | | | | |
| 300 | 6.5 | 28.7 | 8.6 | 24.3 | | | | | | | | | | |
| 400 | 6.2 | 29.2 | 8.2 | 24.8 | 10.9% | 20.4% | | | | | | | | |
| 500 | 6.0 | 29.6 | 8.0 | 25.1 | 10.5 | 20.9 | | | | | | | | |
| 1,000 | 5.7 | 30.0 | 7.6 | 25.8 | 9.8 | 21.8 | 10.9% | 20.1% | 12.3% | 18.2% | | | | |
| 1,500 | 5.6 | 30.1 | 7.4 | 26.0 | 9.6 | 22.1 | 10.6 | 20.4 | 11.9 | 18.7 | | | | |
| 2,000 | 5.6 | 30.2 | 7.4 | 26.0 | 9.5 | 22.2 | 10.5 | 20.6 | 11.7 | 18.9 | 13.0% | 17.2% | | |
| 2,500 | 5.6 | 30.2 | 7.3 | 26.1 | 9.4 | 22.3 | 10.4 | 20.7 | 11.6 | 19.1 | 12.8 | 17.4 | | |
| 3,000 | 5.6 | 30.2 | 7.3 | 26.1 | 9.4 | 22.3 | 10.4 | 20.7 | 11.5 | 19.2 | 12.7 | 17.6 | | |
| 3,500 | 5.5 | 30.2 | 7.3 | 26.2 | 9.3 | 22.4 | 10.3 | 20.8 | 11.4 | 19.2 | 12.6 | 17.7 | | |
| 4,000 | 5.5 | 30.2 | 7.3 | 26.2 | 9.3 | 22.4 | 10.3 | 20.8 | 11.4 | 19.3 | 12.5 | 17.7 | 13.6% | 16.5% |
| 4,500 | 5.5 | 30.2 | 7.2 | 26.2 | 9.3 | 22.4 | 10.3 | 20.8 | 11.4 | 19.3 | 12.5 | 17.8 | 13.5 | 16.6 |
| 5,000 | 5.5 | 30.2 | 7.2 | 26.2 | 9.3 | 22.4 | 10.3 | 20.9 | 11.3 | 19.3 | 12.5 | 17.8 | 13.5 | 16.7 |
| 6,000 | 5.5 | 30.2 | 7.2 | 26.2 | 9.3 | 22.5 | 10.2 | 20.9 | 11.3 | 19.4 | 12.5 | 17.9 | 13.4 | 16.8 |
| 7,000 | 5.5 | 30.2 | 7.2 | 26.3 | 9.2 | 22.5 | 10.2 | 20.9 | 11.3 | 19.4 | 12.4 | 17.9 | 13.3 | 16.8 |
| 8,000 | 5.5 | 30.2 | 7.2 | 26.3 | 9.2 | 22.5 | 10.2 | 20.9 | 11.3 | 19.4 | 12.4 | 17.9 | 13.3 | 16.9 |
| 9,000 | 5.5 | 30.2 | 7.2 | 26.3 | 9.2 | 22.5 | 10.2 | 20.9 | 11.3 | 19.4 | 12.4 | 18.0 | 13.2 | 16.9 |
| 10,000 | 5.5 | 30.2 | 7.2 | 26.3 | 9.2 | 22.5 | 10.2 | 20.9 | 11.2 | 19.4 | 12.4 | 18.0 | 13.2 | 16.9 |
| 15,000 | 5.5 | 30.2 | 7.2 | 26.3 | 9.2 | 22.5 | 10.2 | 21.0 | 11.2 | 19.5 | 12.3 | 18.0 | 13.1 | 17.0 |
| 20,000 | 5.5 | 30.2 | 7.2 | 26.3 | 9.2 | 22.5 | 10.2 | 21.0 | 11.2 | 19.5 | 12.3 | 18.1 | 13.1 | 17.1 |
| 25,000 | 5.5 | 30.2 | 7.2 | 26.3 | 9.2 | 22.6 | 10.2 | 21.0 | 11.2 | 19.5 | 12.3 | 18.1 | 13.1 | 17.1 |
| 50,000 | 5.5 | 30.3 | 7.2 | 26.3 | 9.2 | 22.6 | 10.1 | 21.0 | 11.2 | 19.5 | 12.2 | 18.1 | 13.0 | 17.1 |
| 100,000 | 5.5 | 30.3 | 7.2 | 26.3 | 9.2 | 22.6 | 10.1 | 21.0 | 11.2 | 19.5 | 12.2 | 18.1 | 13.0 | 17.2 |

TABLE 6b

## SAMPLE RELIABILITY FOR RELATIVE FREQUENCIES FOR RANDOM SAMPLES ONLY

*Rate of Occurrence in Sample 0.0%*
*Confidence Level 95%*

| *And Field Size is:* | *For Sample Size of:* 30 | 50 | 100 | 200 | 300 | 500 | 1000 | 2000 |
|---|---|---|---|---|---|---|---|---|
| 200 | 8.8% | 5.0% | 2.1% | | | | | |
| 300 | 9.0 | 5.3 | 2.4 | | | | | |
| 400 | 9.1 | 5.4 | 2.6 | 1.1% | | | | |
| 500 | 9.2 | 5.5 | 2.6 | 1.2 | | | | |
| 1,000 | 9.4 | 5.7 | 2.8 | 1.3 | 0.8% | 0.4% | | |
| 1,500 | 9.4 | 5.7 | 2.9 | 1.4 | 0.9 | 0.5 | | |
| 2,000 | 9.4 | 5.7 | 2.9 | 1.4 | 0.9 | 0.5 | 0.2% | |
| 2,500 | 9.5 | 5.8 | 2.9 | 1.4 | 0.9 | 0.5 | 0.2 | |
| 3,000 | 9.5 | 5.8 | 2.9 | 1.4 | 0.9 | 0.6 | 0.2 | |
| 3,500 | 9.5 | 5.8 | 2.9 | 1.4 | 1.0 | 0.6 | 0.3 | |
| 4,000 | 9.5 | 5.8 | 2.9 | 1.5 | 1.0 | 0.6 | 0.3 | 0.1% |
| 4,500 | 9.5 | 5.8 | 2.9 | 1.5 | 1.0 | 0.6 | 0.3 | 0.1 |
| 5,000 | 9.5 | 5.8 | 2.9 | 1.5 | 1.0 | 0.6 | 0.3 | 0.1 |
| 6,000 | 9.5 | 5.8 | 2.9 | 1.5 | 1.0 | 0.6 | 0.3 | 0.1 |
| 7,000 | 9.5 | 5.8 | 2.9 | 1.5 | 1.0 | 0.6 | 0.3 | 0.1 |
| 8,000 | 9.5 | 5.8 | 2.9 | 1.5 | 1.0 | 0.6 | 0.3 | 0.1 |
| 9,000 | 9.5 | 5.8 | 2.9 | 1.5 | 1.0 | 0.6 | 0.3 | 0.1 |
| 10,000 | 9.5 | 5.8 | 2.9 | 1.5 | 1.0 | 0.6 | 0.3 | 0.1 |
| 15,000 | 9.5 | 5.8 | 2.9 | 1.5 | 1.0 | 0.6 | 0.3 | 0.1 |
| 20,000 | 9.5 | 5.8 | 2.9 | 1.5 | 1.0 | 0.6 | 0.3 | 0.1 |
| 25,000 | 9.5 | 5.8 | 3.0 | 1.5 | 1.0 | 0.6 | 0.3 | 0.1 |
| 50,000 | 9.5 | 5.8 | 3.0 | 1.5 | 1.0 | 0.6 | 0.3 | 0.2 |
| 100,000 | 9.5 | 5.8 | 3.0 | 1.5 | 1.0 | 0.6 | 0.3 | 0.2 |

TABLE 6c

*Rate of Occurrence in Sample 0.0%*
*Confidence Level 99%*

| *And Field Size is:* | *For Sample Size of:* 30 | 50 | 100 | 200 | 300 | 500 | 1000 | 2000 |
|---|---|---|---|---|---|---|---|---|
| 200 | 13.1% | 7.6% | 3.2% | | | | | |
| 300 | 13.5 | 8.0 | 3.7 | | | | | |
| 400 | 13.7 | 8.2 | 3.9 | 1.6% | | | | |
| 500 | 13.8 | 8.4 | 4.0 | 1.8 | | | | |
| 1,000 | 14.0 | 8.6 | 4.3 | 2.0 | 1.3% | 0.6% | | |
| 1,500 | 14.1 | 8.7 | 4.4 | 2.1 | 1.4 | 0.8 | | |
| 2,000 | 14.1 | 8.7 | 4.4 | 2.2 | 1.4 | 0.8 | 0.3% | |
| 2,500 | 14.2 | 8.7 | 4.4 | 2.2 | 1.4 | 0.8 | 0.4 | |
| 3,000 | 14.2 | 8.7 | 4.4 | 2.2 | 1.5 | 0.8 | 0.4 | |
| 3,500 | 14.2 | 8.7 | 4.4 | 2.2 | 1.5 | 0.9 | 0.4 | |
| 4,000 | 14.2 | 8.7 | 4.4 | 2.2 | 1.5 | 0.9 | 0.4 | 0.2% |
| 4,500 | 14.2 | 8.8 | 4.5 | 2.2 | 1.5 | 0.9 | 0.4 | 0.2 |
| 5,000 | 14.2 | 8.8 | 4.5 | 2.2 | 1.5 | 0.9 | 0.4 | 0.2 |
| 6,000 | 14.2 | 8.8 | 4.5 | 2.2 | 1.5 | 0.9 | 0.4 | 0.2 |
| 7,000 | 14.2 | 8.8 | 4.5 | 2.2 | 1.5 | 0.9 | 0.4 | 0.2 |
| 8,000 | 14.2 | 8.8 | 4.5 | 2.3 | 1.5 | 0.9 | 0.4 | 0.2 |
| 9,000 | 14.2 | 8.8 | 4.5 | 2.3 | 1.5 | 0.9 | 0.4 | 0.2 |
| 10,000 | 14.2 | 8.8 | 4.5 | 2.3 | 1.5 | 0.9 | 0.4 | 0.2 |
| 15,000 | 14.2 | 8.8 | 4.5 | 2.3 | 1.5 | 0.9 | 0.4 | 0.2 |
| 20,000 | 14.2 | 8.8 | 4.5 | 2.3 | 1.5 | 0.9 | 0.5 | 0.2 |
| 25,000 | 14.2 | 8.8 | 4.5 | 2.3 | 1.5 | 0.9 | 0.5 | 0.2 |
| 50,000 | 14.2 | 8.8 | 4.5 | 2.3 | 1.5 | 0.9 | 0.5 | 0.2 |
| 100,000 | 14.2 | 8.8 | 4.5 | 2.3 | 1.5 | 0.9 | 0.5 | 0.2 |

## TABLE 7

## SAMPLE RELIABILITY FOR AVERAGE VALUES FOR RANDOM SAMPLES ONLY

| *When Sample Size is:* | *For Confidence Levels of:* 95% | 99% | 99.9% |
|---|---|---|---|
| | *Sampling Error as Multiple of Standard Deviation* | | |
| | *Field Size is 500* | | |
| 50 | .2630 | .3455 | .4414 |
| 100 | .1753 | .2304 | .2943 |
| 150 | .1339 | .1760 | .2248 |
| 200 | .1074 | .1413 | .1802 |
| | *Field Size is 1000* | | |
| 50 | .2702 | .3551 | .4535 |
| 100 | .1859 | .2444 | .3121 |
| 150 | .1475 | .1939 | .2477 |
| 200 | .1240 | .1629 | .2081 |
| 300 | .0947 | .1244 | .1589 |
| 400 | .0759 | .0998 | .1274 |
| | *Field Size is 2000* | | |
| 50 | .2737 | .3597 | .4594 |
| 100 | .1910 | .2511 | .3207 |
| 150 | .1539 | .2023 | .2584 |
| 200 | .1314 | .1728 | .2205 |
| 300 | .1043 | .1371 | .1751 |
| 400 | .0877 | .1152 | .1471 |
| 500 | .0759 | .0998 | .1274 |
| 600 | .0670 | .0880 | .1124 |
| 700 | .0597 | .0785 | .1003 |
| 800 | .0537 | .0705 | .0901 |
| 900 | .0484 | .0637 | .0813 |

## SAMPLE RELIABILITY FOR AVERAGE VALUES
## FOR RANDOM SAMPLES ONLY

| *When Sample Size is:* | *For Confidence Levels of:* 95% | 99% | 99.9% |
|---|---|---|---|
| | *Sampling Error as Multiple of Standard Deviation* | | |
| | *Field Size is 3000* | | |
| 50 | .2749 | .3612 | .4614 |
| 100 | .1927 | .2533 | .3235 |
| 150 | .1560 | .2050 | .2618 |
| 200 | .1339 | .1760 | .2248 |
| 300 | .1074 | .1411 | .1802 |
| 400 | .0912 | .1199 | .1532 |
| 500 | .0800 | .1052 | .1343 |
| 600 | .0716 | .0941 | .1202 |
| 700 | .0649 | .0853 | .1089 |
| 800 | .0594 | .0780 | .0996 |
| 900 | .0547 | .0718 | .0918 |
| 1,000 | .0506 | .0665 | .0850 |
| | *Field Size is 4000* | | |
| 50 | .2754 | .3621 | .4624 |
| 100 | .1935 | .2544 | .3249 |
| 150 | .1570 | .2063 | .2635 |
| 200 | .1351 | .1775 | .2267 |
| 300 | .1088 | .1430 | .1827 |
| 400 | .0930 | .1222 | .1561 |
| 500 | .0820 | .1077 | .1376 |
| 600 | .0738 | .0970 | .1238 |
| 700 | .0673 | .0884 | .1130 |
| 800 | .0620 | .0815 | .1040 |
| 900 | .0575 | .0756 | .0965 |
| 1,000 | .0537 | .0705 | .0901 |
| 1,100 | .0503 | .0661 | .0845 |
| 1,200 | .0473 | .0622 | .0794 |
| 1,300 | .0447 | .0587 | .0749 |
| 1,400 | .0422 | .0555 | .0709 |
| 1,500 | .0400 | .0526 | .0672 |

TABLE 7 (Continued)

## SAMPLE RELIABILITY FOR AVERAGE VALUES
## FOR RANDOM SAMPLES ONLY

| *When Sample Size is:* | *For Confidence Levels of:* 95% | 99% | 99.9% |
|---|---|---|---|
| | *Sampling Error as Multiple of Standard Deviation* | | |
| | *Field Size is 5000* | | |
| 50 | .2758 | .3225 | .4629 |
| 100 | .1940 | .2550 | .3257 |
| 150 | .1576 | .2071 | .2646 |
| 200 | .1358 | .1785 | .2279 |
| 300 | .1097 | .1442 | .1842 |
| 400 | .0940 | .1235 | .1578 |
| 500 | .0832 | .1093 | .1396 |
| 600 | .0751 | .0987 | .1260 |
| 700 | .0687 | .0903 | .1153 |
| 800 | .0635 | .0835 | .1066 |
| 900 | .0592 | .0778 | .0993 |
| 1,000 | .0554 | .0729 | .0931 |
| 1,100 | .0522 | .0686 | .0876 |
| 1,200 | .0493 | .0648 | .0828 |
| 1,300 | .0468 | .0615 | .0785 |
| 1,400 | .0444 | .0584 | .0746 |
| 1,500 | .0424 | .0557 | .0711 |
| 2,000 | .0339 | .0446 | .0570 |
| | *Field Size is 10,000* | | |
| 50 | .2765 | .3635 | .4641 |
| 100 | .1950 | .2563 | .3274 |
| 150 | .1588 | .2087 | .2666 |
| 200 | .1372 | .1803 | .2303 |
| 300 | .1114 | .1465 | .1871 |
| 400 | .0960 | .1262 | .1612 |
| 500 | .0854 | .1123 | .1434 |
| 600 | .0776 | .1020 | .1302 |
| 700 | .0715 | .0939 | .1199 |
| 800 | .0665 | .0874 | .1116 |
| 900 | .0623 | .0819 | .1046 |
| 1,000 | .0588 | .0773 | .0987 |
| 1,100 | .0557 | .0733 | .0936 |
| 1,200 | .0531 | .0698 | .0891 |
| 1,300 | .0507 | .0666 | .0851 |
| 1,400 | .0486 | .0638 | .0815 |
| 1,500 | .0467 | .0613 | .0783 |
| 2,000 | .0392 | .0515 | .0658 |
| 2,500 | .0339 | .0446 | .0570 |
| 3,000 | .0299 | .0393 | .0502 |
| 3,500 | .0267 | .0351 | .0449 |
| 4,000 | .0240 | .0315 | .0403 |

TABLE 7 (Continued)

## SAMPLE RELIABILITY FOR AVERAGE VALUES FOR RANDOM SAMPLES ONLY

| *When Sample Size is:* | *For Confidence Levels of:* 95% | 99% | 99.9% |
|---|---|---|---|
| | *Sampling Error as Multiple of Standard Deviation* | | |
| *Field Size is 20,000* | | | |
| 50 | .2768 | .3639 | .4647 |
| 100 | .1955 | .2570 | .3282 |
| 150 | .1594 | .2095 | .2676 |
| 200 | .1379 | .1812 | .2315 |
| 300 | .1123 | .1476 | .1885 |
| 400 | .0970 | .1275 | .1628 |
| 500 | .0866 | .1138 | .1453 |
| 600 | .0788 | .1036 | .1323 |
| 700 | .0728 | .0956 | .1222 |
| 800 | .0679 | .0892 | .1140 |
| 900 | .0638 | .0839 | .1072 |
| 1,000 | .0604 | .0794 | .1014 |
| 1,100 | .0574 | .0755 | .0964 |
| 1,200 | .0548 | .0721 | .0921 |
| 1,300 | .0526 | .0691 | .0882 |
| 1,400 | .0505 | .0664 | .0848 |
| 1,500 | .0487 | .0640 | .0817 |
| 2,000 | .0416 | .0546 | .0698 |
| 2,500 | .0367 | .0482 | .0615 |
| 3,000 | .0330 | .0434 | .0553 |
| 3,500 | .0301 | .0395 | .0505 |
| 4,000 | .0277 | .0364 | .0465 |
| 4,500 | .0257 | .0338 | .0431 |
| 5,000 | .0240 | .0315 | .0403 |
| 6,000 | .0212 | .0278 | .0356 |
| 7,000 | .0189 | .0248 | .0317 |
| 8,000 | .0170 | .0223 | .0285 |
| 9,000 | .0153 | .0201 | .0257 |

## SAMPLE RELIABILITY FOR AVERAGE VALUES FOR RANDOM SAMPLES ONLY

| *When Sample Size is:* | *For Confidence Levels of:* 95% | 99% | 99.9% |
|---|---|---|---|
| | *Sampling Error as Multiple of Standard Deviation* | | |
| | *Field Size is 100,000* | | |
| 50 | .2771 | .3643 | .4652 |
| 100 | .1959 | .2576 | .3288 |
| 150 | .1599 | .2102 | .2684 |
| 200 | .1385 | .1820 | .2324 |
| 300 | .1130 | .1485 | .1897 |
| 400 | .0978 | .1285 | .1642 |
| 500 | .0874 | .1149 | .1468 |
| 600 | .0798 | .1048 | .1339 |
| 700 | .0738 | .0970 | .1239 |
| 800 | .0690 | .0907 | .1159 |
| 900 | .0650 | .0855 | .1092 |
| 1,000 | .0617 | .0810 | .1035 |
| 1,100 | .0588 | .0772 | .0986 |
| 1,200 | .0562 | .0739 | .0944 |
| 1,300 | .0540 | .0710 | .0906 |
| 1,400 | .0520 | .0684 | .0873 |
| 1,500 | .0502 | .0660 | .0843 |
| 2,000 | .0434 | .0570 | .0728 |
| 2,500 | .0387 | .0509 | .0650 |
| 3,000 | .0352 | .0463 | .0591 |
| 3,500 | .0326 | .0428 | .0547 |
| 4,000 | .0304 | .0399 | .0510 |
| 4,500 | .0285 | .0375 | .0479 |
| 5,000 | .0270 | .0355 | .0453 |
| 6,000 | .0246 | .0322 | .0412 |
| 7,000 | .0226 | .0297 | .0379 |
| 8,000 | .0210 | .0276 | .0353 |
| 9,000 | .0197 | .0259 | .0331 |
| 10,000 | .0186 | .0244 | .0312 |
| 20,000 | .0124 | .0163 | .0208 |

# *Appendix*

The following information and formulae may give some idea of the principles on which these tables were based.

## TABLE 2: *Sample Sizes for Sampling Attributes*

These tables were computed from the formula for the standard error of a percent for a sample drawn from a finite population where p is assumed to be the maximum value shown in the heading (50%, 10%, 5%, or 2%). The formula used is:

$$\pm E = t\sqrt{\frac{pq}{n}\left(\frac{N-n}{N-1}\right)}$$

p is as described above

q is $1-p$

n is the sample size

N is the field size

t is a factor related to the confidence level (2.58 for the 99% confidence level and 1.96 for the 95% confidence level).

This formula is based on the mathematical theory of probability. It provides a measure of the amount of variability to be expected in samples drawn on a random basis with respect to some event which occurs with frequency p in the population or field. For instance, if a jar contains N well-mixed balls of which p percent are black and q percent are white, the range of variation in the proportion of black balls in samples of size n with a probability fixed by t will be given by this formula.

For a discussion of the formula see:

Vance, L. L. and Neter, J., *Statistical Sampling for Auditors and Accountants,* John Wiley & Sons, Inc., N. Y., 1956, pp. 183-185.

Wallis, W. A. and Roberts, H. V., *Statistics, a New Approach,* Free Press, Glencoe, Ill., 1956, pp. 375-379.

Neter, J. and Wasserman, W., *Fundamental Statistics for Business and Economics,* Allyn and Bacon, Inc., N. Y., 1956, pp. 342-343.

## TABLE 3: FACTORS FOR ESTIMATING THE STANDARD DEVIATION

The factors given for the conversion of the average range of several groups of size n to an estimate of the population standard deviation are based on the relationship of the average of the sampling distribution of the range of groups of values to the standard deviation of the population from which the sample groups were drawn.

The development of the numerical values given in the table is quite complex, involving both higher mathematics and advanced statistical methods.

For those who have a sufficient background in these areas to follow the development, the following discussions are suggested:

Hald, A., *Statistical Theory with Engineering Applications,* John Wiley & Sons, Inc., N. Y., 1952, pp. 319-322.

Burr, I. W., *Engineering Statistics and Quality Control,* McGraw-Hill Book Company, Inc., N. Y., 1953, pp. 177-178.

## TABLE 4: SAMPLE SIZES FOR ESTIMATING AVERAGE VALUES

The sampling variability of an average (arithmetic mean) of a sample or the expected variation with a given probability of the means of samples drawn at random from a given population about the mean of the population may be computed from:

$$\pm E = t \frac{\sigma}{\sqrt{n}} \sqrt{\frac{N - n}{N - 1}}$$

where

- t is a factor related to the confidence level (1.96 for the 95% confidence level, 2.58 for the 99% confidence level and 3.3 for the 99.9% confidence level)
- $\sigma$ is a measure (standard deviation of the variability of the values comprising the field (population)
- n is the number of values in the sample
- N is the number of values in the field

Conversely, it follows that samples drawn from a population with mean $\bar{X}$ will not differ from that mean by more than $\pm E$ with a probability that this departure will not exceed this value fixed by the value of t (confidence level).

Table 2b provides the solution of this formula for various field sizes (N) and sample sizes (n) based on the assumption that the standard deviation ($\sigma$) is equal to one. To obtain a measure of the sampling variability of the mean of a sample drawn from a field for which the standard deviation is estimated (Table 2a) to be $\sigma$, the value in the table is multiplied by the value of the estimated standard deviation.

Discussions of the theory underlying the sampling variability of an average appear in all statistics textbooks. Some suggested readings are given below:

Arkin, H. and Colton, R. R., *Statistical Methods,* 4th Revised Edition, Barnes & Noble, Inc., N. Y., 1957, pp. 113-118.

Mills, F. C., *Statistical Methods,* 3rd Edition, Henry Holt and Co., N. Y., 1955, Chapter 7.

Hansen, M. H., Hurwitz, W. H. and Madow, W. G., *Sample Survey Methods and Theory,* Volume I, John Wiley & Sons, Inc., N. Y., 1953, Chapter 4.

Vance, L. L. and Neter, J., *Statistical Sampling for Auditors and Accountants,* John Wiley & Sons, Inc., 1956, Chapters 9 and 10.

## TABLE 5: PROBABILITIES OF INCLUDING AT LEAST ONE OCCURRENCE IN A SAMPLE

The values in this table express the probability of obtaining at least one item of a specific type in sample size n when this type occurs in the field size N in proportion p.

The computation is accomplished by computing the probability that none of these events will be included in the sample and subtracting the result from 100% (or 1.0).

The formula is:

$$\text{Probability} = 1.0 - \frac{C_{o}^{pN} \cdot C_{n}^{qN}}{C_{n}^{N}}$$

where

$C^N_n$ represents the number of possible combinations of N items taken n at a time

p is proportion of event in the field

q is proportion of event not in field

N is the number of items in the field

n is the number of items in the sample

For a detailed discussion of the theory and method see:

Grant, E. L., *Statistical Quality Control,* McGraw-Hill Book Co., New York, 1952, 2nd Edition, Chapter IX.

## TABLE 6: SAMPLE RELIABILITY FOR RELATIVE FREQUENCIES FOR RANDOM SAMPLES ONLY

Tables 6 and 6a are computed on the basis of the binomial distribution for the infinite population case and from the hypergeometrical distribution for the finite population.

Values for the binomial distribution were obtained from *Tables for Use with Binomial Samples,* Mainland, D., Herrera, L., and Sutcliffe, M. I., New York University College of Medicine, 1956.

For the sample from a finite population, values are computed from the solution of the formula for each term of the hypergeometric distribution and are given in terms of the probability that the sample is within the limits stated. The formula for each term of the hypergeometric distribution is:

$$P_r = \frac{C^{pN}_r \, C^{qN}_{n-r}}{C^N_n}$$

where

$C^N_n$ represents the number of possible combinations of N items taken n at a time

p is proportion of events in the field

q is proportion of field without events

N is the field size

n is the sample size

r is number of events in sample

$P_r$ is probability of obtaining sample of size n with r events from field of size N when field contains proportion p of events

By cumulating the probabilities for each term of the distribution toward the center (mean) from each end, the limits may be secured when probabilities equivalent to 1-$\alpha$ are cumulated (where $\alpha$ is confidence level).

Tables 4c and 4d were computed in a similar fashion and give the value of the population with the proportion for which the probability of generating a sample with zero defects is 1-$\alpha$ where $\alpha$ is the confidence level.

## TABLE 7: SAMPLE RELIABILITY FOR AVERAGE VALUES FOR RANDOM SAMPLES ONLY

*Table 7 is the inverse computation of the formula given for Table 4.*